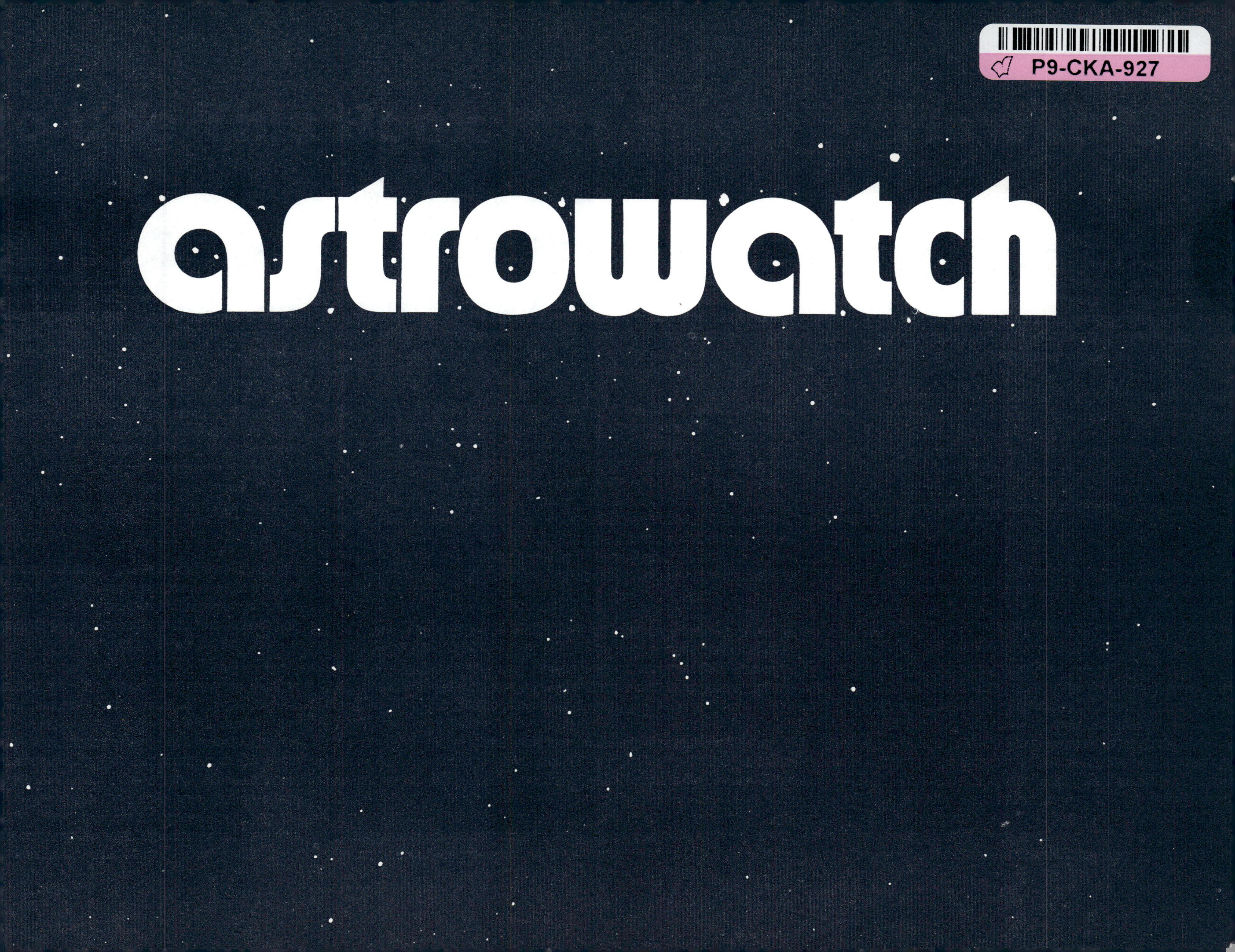
astrowatch

N
M8
SAGITTARIUS

astrowatch

BEN MAYER,
A.R.C.A.
author of STARWATCH and HALLEY'S COMET FINDER

A PERIGEE BOOK

For Shawn Christopher
and Heather Melissa

Perigee Books
are published by
The Putnam Publishing Group
200 Madison Avenue
New York, NY 10016

Published simultaneously in Canada.

Cover design, back cover design and photos by Ben Mayer.
Book design by Ben Mayer and Arlene Goldberg.
Illustrations, Stellaphane™ starmaps, and astrophotography by Ben Mayer.

Library of Congress Cataloging-in-Publication Data

Mayer, Ben.
Astrowatch / Ben Mayer.
p. cm.
"A Perigee book."
ISBN 0-399-51431-7
1. Constellations—Amateurs' manuals. I. Title.
QB63.M4448 1988 87-25172 CIP
523—dc19

Typeset by Fisher Composition, Inc.

Printed in the United States of America
1 2 3 4 5 6 7 8 9 10

The author wishes to thank Stephen J. Edberg, science coordinator for comet rendezvous and asteroid flyby missions at the NASA Jet Propulsion Laboratory in Pasadena, California, for proofreading the astronomical text and making welcome suggestions and corrections.

Gratitude is also due to Dr. Ariel A. Bloch, professor of Semitic linguistics, Department of Near Eastern Studies, University of California at Berkeley, for his assistance with the "Beyond Genesis" chapter (pages 124–128).

I am indebted to Susie Antillon, for deciphering my handwritten manuscript and turning it into a legible computer typescript.

Thank you, Lucille, my love, for insisting that April comes before July and for helping me stay in sequence with the stars.

Contents

Foreword

Since earliest times, humankind has looked to the sun and the stars for guidance. With the passage of time, measured by solar comings and goings, reasons were sought in the heavens for our very existence.

Divinity was given to the warm, light-giving sun by day. At night, God—many gods—were installed among the stars and the mysterious wandering planets. Supremely powerful celestial deities, ever-present and visible, lay far beyond reach until graven terrestrial images yielded to abstract ideas.

Occult influence on earthly and human affairs began to be assumed and explored.

Civilizations created structure with different religions, but even enlightenment could not conquer inborn fear. Terror of the unknown turned to profound awe and sometimes led the way to reverence.

In Western lands, the church took upon itself the central position of universal authority. It is wrong to refer to the church (from the Greek *kyros* = "power") as though it were some remote, untouchable body. From the outset, it consisted of ordinary and extraordinary human beings: farmers, priests, carpenters, and popes. The church embraced good Samaritans and bloodthirsty inquisitors, queens or kings, masters and slaves, but all were souls dwelling in mortal bodies just like you and me. Often power was greater than ability, or greed and brutality outweighed charity and love.

With reformation came knowledge, the vanguard of science. In league with technology, science assumed authority based on its invaluable contributions to the family of man.

Here again, we should not regard science (from the Latin *scientia* = "having knowledge") as an abstract thing. Science comprises extraordinary minds, often dwelling in ordinary persons, inventors, prodigies, charlatans or rogues. Scientists embody humility and modesty as well as unspeakable vanity or conceit. Science conquered childbed fever and polio, but it also spawned napalm flamethrowers and the atom bomb.

Scientific practitioners arrogantly claim for themselves powers that were once vested in the church, and hide behind a mantle of secrecy when challenged.

For the future, moral values alone may decide our destiny in the universe. Ethical conduct must answer the questions of what is right or wrong, good or bad. Our instinctive preoccupation with the stars still stems from ancient, deep-rooted feelings that the solution to all our problems may yet be found "out there." It appears that our fascination with the extraterrestrial is still derived from our hope for guidance from the stars.

For the time being and into the foreseeable future, we will have to live with fellow space travelers and our fragile ecological resources, here on planet earth. Deep in our hearts, most of us know what is right and what is wrong. The golden rule was already taught twenty-five hundred years ago by Confucius, the Chinese philosopher:

> Do not do unto others what you do not want done to yourself.

Think about it.

Law of the Bumblebee

If the common bumblebee (genus *Bombus*) knew the laws of aerodynamics, it would realize that it cannot possibly fly. Bumblebees might sense that to support flight their tiny wings have to move at impossible speeds to sustain the weight of their massive bodies in the air. But yet bumblebees fly.

Had I known the rules of astrophotography, which maintain that it is impossible to take pictures of the nightsky from a light-polluted city, I would not have recorded thirteen exposures revealing the growing outburst of a nova in the Milky Way.

Never would I have taken photograph after photograph of this cataclysmic explosion in deep space from the roof of my house in West Los Angeles.

Ignorance with serendipity[1] can be bliss.

[1] The gift of finding valuable things not sought for.

How to Use This Book

This astronomy book is new in many ways. The contents, the format and the ideas expressed present a departure from convention. Up until today it was as if nobody below the equator viewed the stars at all. Subtly a concept was introduced that you have to be a dweller in the northern hemisphere to be concerned with the starry heavens. No longer.

The Starfield maps in *Astrowatch* are shown from two different viewpoints. The reverse images (white stars against a blue-black sky) are printed as they appear to persons living in Australia, New Zealand or in South America. The negative, more detailed constellations (black stars on a white background), show the sky in the conventional "North up" manner. These are presented to favor northern-hemisphere observers in North America, Europe, or in Asia.

When you look at these maps closely, you will note that it was not just a matter of turning the photographs upside down, which could be construed as achieving the same purpose. The starfields are printed with identification and key stars in their correct orientation as they appear in the sky when seen from "down under."

Often this writer has stood with his head between his legs to recognize the Sagittarius "teapot" from Tahiti, or the Scorpion from the plains of New South Wales. A friend and mentor, Dr. William Liller, former professor of astronomy at Harvard University, confided to me that when he first moved south to the Chilean Andes, he had to "learn the sky all over again," to reacquaint himself with the familiar constellations, as seen from the southern hemisphere. We should think of our globe as "spaceship earth" in terms of a giant sphere hurtling through the universe. The sky appears different depending upon your point of view.

Such signs of northern prejudice can be found in most books on astronomy, certainly in all "atlantes" (plural of atlas) where, since ancient times, a northern chauvinism was practiced. You can check for this form of bias yourself where maps and diagrams of large areas are always oriented for northern starwatchers. (For small, limited fields of view, the "north-up" convention may still be observed.)

Another such sign of prejudice concerns gender in science. While we may know that Mrs. Curie was one of the greatest scientists of all time, it almost seems that her name was Madame Curie, as if the first name was "Madame." The fact that she was named Marja Skłodowska Curie is almost forgotten. When in 1898 she found a new metal she called it "Polonium" in honor of her native country of Poland. She went on to receive the Nobel Prize for Chemistry in 1911 and was the first woman honored with membership in the French Academy of Medicine and a professorship at the Sorbonne University. She became far more famous than her husband Pierre.

Similarly when Darwin is spoken of, the only name given is Charles Robert Darwin. His monkeys are almost better known than the fact that this very reverent man was married. His wife, Frances, worked with him throughout his pioneering years, collaborating on much of his famous research.

Finally, the last and perhaps the most important new feature in *Astrowatch* concerns fundamental human belief. God is mentioned in this book on astronomy. Check in the index under G for God.

There is a purpose to the form of the book you hold in your hands. Its very shape represents an idea.

ASTROWATCH was created to bring the stars to you, to place the very heavens into your hands in the accepted standard scale of a piece of writing paper. Even the horizontal layout is *no accident,* but was chosen *by design.* It relates to the horizon—the apparent junction of earth and sky. The 11-by-8½-inch format is not a publisher's random selection, but the choice of a "designing" author. By practicing forethought, we have related the earth on which we live to the heavens beyond to better understand the sky. If you let the horizontal and vertical sizes of any page represent two of our known dimensions, width and height, you only need one more measure to place you "in space" as we understand it today.

The width of any page represents *the first dimension,* right and left or east and west. Such "orientation" can make us face toward the Orient. That is where the main walls or chief altars in houses of prayer can still be found, and where millions of worshipers daily address their prayers.

The height of our pages serves to project *the second dimension,* north and south, with the northern compass point conventionally represented by the tops of most pages. Even maps of the Southern Hemisphere (below the earth's equator) follow this convention long ago established by mariners.

The third dimension known today, the "in and out" of space, is determined by the distance between the eye of the beholder and an object. For scientific purposes, this should not be left to chance. It relates to the *field of view* of the human eye. When inventors of cameras standardized their lenses and viewfinders, they concurred that this region is shaped like a page in this book. In this area, the human eye (in conjunction with the miraculous human brain) perceives depth by experience.

Drawings and photographs have taught us to combine all three dimensions for standard or average perception through our minds. Still, most astronomical or astrological material is actually presented in two-dimensional form. It is in this area that the illustrations and photographs in *Astrowatch* present a new concept, a departure from conventional books concerning the stars and the sky. In order for anyone to be able to visualize and participate in the use of these pages, we must establish the "depth" of its third dimension. To make this a "three-dimensional" book, you should view it from a distance of 15–18 inches (38–46 centimeters).

Now the starcharts of the zodiacal constellations will be seen and perceived exactly as they appear in the heavens, one window area at a time. Human eyes can only concentrate and focus attention on small areas at once. Surrounding fields may be generally perceived, but attention is normally confined to one constellation per viewing.

The twelve zodiacal starfields present themselves naturally over the period of one year. We should have ample time to view each and every one at our leisure, one per month. To help you find constellations at their *culminations,* when they are highest in your sky, different observing times are offered (see pages 10–11). For long winter nights, up to eleven date/hour periods are listed per constellation. For shorter summer nights, nine date/hour windows are suggested, from first darkness after twilight to dawn on the next day.

The following pages will allow you to plan ahead—even to avoid bright moonlight or cloudy nights. There is not only a wide selection of observing hours, but a range of up to five months during which you can view any of the starfields of your choice.

You will require only one optical instrument. It is the most wonderful device fashioned by nature, the human eye. You may want to use it in conjunction with an optional pair of binoculars. In either case good care should be taken of your gift of vision and its optic organ, especially as concerns its adaption to the dark. (See "Adapting to the Dark," page 130.) With the wide range of observing times, you may elect to observe near midnight or even just before dawn. If you set an alarm clock to wake you, please turn on no white lights. Prepare a red-shielded flashlight before you retire because your eyes will be well rested and dark adapted upon rising from sleep. Have everything you may need ready to go and observe after you dress warmly in total darkness.

Constellation	Year-round culmination dates/hours before midnight				
	19:00 hours	20:00 hours	21:00 hours	22:00 hours	23:00 hours
Pisces	December 15 to January 1	December 1 to December 15	November 15 to December 1	November 1 to November 15	October 15 to November 1
Aries	January 1 to January 15	December 15 to January 1	December 1 to December 15	November 15 to December 1	November 1 to November 15
Taurus	February 15 to March 1	February 1 to February 15	January 15 to February 1	January 1 to January 15	December 15 to January 1
Gemini	March 15 to April 1	March 1 to March 15	February 15 to March 1	February 1 to February 15	January 15 to February 1
Cancer	May 1 to May 15*	April 15 to May 1*	March 15 to April 1 April 1 to April 15	March 1 to March 15	February 15 to March 1
Leo	June 1 to June 15*	May 15 to June 1*	May 1 to May 15*	April 15 to May 1*	March 15 to April 1 April 1 to April 15*
Virgo	July 15 to August 1*	July 1 to July 15*	June 15 to July 1*	June 1 to June 15*	May 15 to June 1*
Libra	August 1 to August 15*	July 15 to August 1*	July 1 to July 15*	June 15 to July 1*	June 1 to June 15*
Scorpius	September 1 to September 15*	August 15 to September 1*	August 1 to August 15*	July 15 to August 1*	July 1 to July 15*
Sagittarius	October 1 to October 15*	September 15 to October 1*	September 1 to September 15*	August 15 to September 1*	August 1 to August 15*
Capricorn	October 15 to November 1	End of daylight saving time. Fall back one hour to standard time	October 1 to October 15*	September 15 to October 1*	September 1 to September 15*
Aquarius	November 1 to November 15	October 15 to November 1	End of daylight saving time. Fall back one hour to standard time	October 1 to October 15*	September 15 to October 1*

*Times on these dates are adjusted for daylight saving times.

Year-round culmination dates/hours after midnight

Midnight	01:00 hours	02:00 hours	03:00 hours	04:00 hours	05:00 hours	Abbre-viations
End of daylight saving time. Fall back one hour to standard time.	October 1 to October 15*	September 15 to October 1*	September 1 to September 15*	August 15 to September 1*	August 1 to August 15*	PSC
October 15 to November 1	End of daylight saving time. Fall back one hour to standard time.	October 1 to October 15*	September 15 to October 1*	September 1 to September 15*	August 15 to September 1*	ARI
December 1 to December 15	November 15 to December 1	November 1 to November 15	October 15 to November 1	End of daylight saving time. Fall back one hour to standard time	October 1 to October 15*	TAU
January 1 to January 15	December 15 to January 1	December 1 to December 15	November 15 to December 1	November 1 to November 15	October 15 to November 1	GEM
February 1 to February 15	January 15 to February 1	January 1 to January 15	December 15 to January 1	December 1 to December 15	November 15 to December 1	CNC
March 1 to March 15	February 15 to March 1	February 1 to February 15	January 15 to February 1	January 1 to January 15	December 15 to January 1	LEO
May 1 to May 15*	April 15 to May 1*	March 15 to April 1 April 1 to April 15*	March 1 to March 15	February 15 to March 1	February 1 to February 15	VIR
May 15 to June 1*	May 1 to May 15*	April 15 to May 1*	March 15 to April 1 April 1 to April 15*	March 1 to March 15	February 15 to March 1	LIB
June 15 to July 1*	June 1 to June 15*	May 15 to June 1*	May 1 to May 15*	April 15 to May 1*	March 15 to April 1 April 1 to April 15*	SCO
July 15 to August 1*	July 1 to July 15*	June 15 to July 1*	June 1 to June 15*	May 15 to June 1*	May 1 to May 15*	SGR
August 15 to September 1*	August 1 to August 15*	July 15 to August 1*	July 1 to July 15*	June 15 to July 1*	June 1 to June 15*	CAP
September 1 to September 15*	August 15 to September 1*	August 1 to August 15*	July 15 to August 1*	July 1 to July 15*	June 15 to July 1*	AQR

Remember: in SPRING, "spring" forward one hour, in FALL, "fall" backward one hour.

In the Beginning

The inspiring story of the stars must be simply told; it forms a vital focus to our lives. We may all share the majesty of the heavens. Let us ignore the prejudice of those who cast occult horoscopes and the disdain of aloof science.

One must never forget that the discipline of astronomy has its roots deep in ancient observational astrology. Modern astrophysicists owe much to unsung starwatchers who nightly stood atop the highest platforms of ziggurats (pyramid-shaped temples) in historic Babylon. Between the Persian rivers Euphrates and Tigris, the stars were observed as they rose unfailingly above far horizons until they set at dawn. In the distant East, Chinese stargazers were also beginning to collect their own invaluable first records. That was some five thousand years ago, when humankind was young.

The earliest astrologers were archetypal observers who sensed the urgent call of the stars, as many of us are drawn skyward again today. We feel that our beginnings lie deep in distant space. Through the study of atoms and chemistry, we can even deduce that our very bodies are created of the stuff that makes up the stars themselves. With radio receivers, we can listen to the faint echoes of the *big bang,* the primordial explosion that triggered the creation of the universe perhaps some eighteen billion years ago.

Our own cosmic neighborhood was not even formed until thirteen billion years after this cataclysmic first moment of Genesis. On a modern time scale, it was as if the "big bang" had occurred at the stroke of midnight last night and, until late this afternoon, there was not even a solar system, neither heaven nor earth.

In the beginning there had been hydrogen and some helium, the biblical "face of the waters." By this evening, the glorious sun was created upon the dark of the deep. The stars began to shine in the firmament. On this time measure, the two brief seconds before today's midnight can be said to constitute all the centuries during which intelligent humans have evolved on earth: two short moments representing the entire lifespan of *Homo sapiens* and his ancestors on our planet. From Adam and Eve to Albert Einstein and Marie Curie, from Noah's ark to manned spaceships on the moon, the millennia since Babylonian priests kept their astrological vigils are as brief as the wink of an eye—a short fraction of a second.

Early wisdom could not grasp that our sun was merely one of the countless stellar bodies that seemed to rise in the east and set in the west. It was not yet understood that our life-giving sun is our nearest star. Astronomers classify old Sol as a *yellow dwarf.* As with all stars, the life of the sun is finite and must come to an end. In about five billion years, the nuclear solar fires will "turn nova," then burn out and die. Earth will have been scorched to a crisp and the oceans will have evaporated before freezing into oblivion.

Still, the ratio of past intelligent lifetimes to the span of the future remains truly astronomical: two seconds to some twenty-four thousand seconds. For the solar system, the end will come an eternity hence. On the Genesis scale of time, it will occur some time tomorrow morning.

The sun is merely an average star with a planetary system that occupies a tiny space near the edge of our galaxy, the Milky Way. Thus, our nearest star with its nine known major satellites is only a single sun among the estimated hundred billion stars in our galaxy. The vast Milky Way galaxy itself is only one among myriad galaxies. Such galactic "island universes," each one containing thousands of millions or hundreds of thousands of millions of stars, may remain concealed far outside our capacity to see.

There is so much more to the stars than ever meets the eye. For every source of light we see in the heavens, there are countless more that shine beyond our sight, but not past our imagination.

On pondering the cosmos, those who stand on the cutting edge of research cannot lose sight of how limited our knowledge is. In terms of what there is to learn, the most gifted astronomer knows as little as the humble amateurs whose love (from the latin *amare*, "to love") makes them seek out the stars.

In the contemplation of the heavens, we must draw on our most sensitive and creative resources: our mind's eye and our souls. We should not only look, but try to see and feel. Here our own talents may surpass the perceptions of the world's foremost scientists, their telescopes—even their insights.

Take heart: only two Genesis seconds have passed symbolizing the time of intelligent terrestrial life. Think of where we may be just one second hence, in A.D. 200,000. Breathtaking futures lie ahead.

The stars can be approached from two different perspectives: astrology or astronomy. The oldest method, of course, is the astrological. Then, over the ages, astronomy grew from observational disciplines into knowledge of the celestial bodies. Astronomy is regarded as the oldest science known to humankind. Most star-related teachings trace their roots to observations, many of which can be repeated and practiced by one and all today.

There seems to be little harmony between practitioners of astronomy and astrology. Yet to pursue one path while ignoring the other appears narrow-minded—or even blind. In these highly visual fields, it is like concentrating on *sight* while forgetting *vision.*

Over the millennia, once-popular astrology has lost its observational emphasis and has turned increasingly toward theory. It has speculated on the divination of the supposed influences of the stars on human affairs and on terrestrial events. It is the stellar horoscope positions with their relationships to the planets that have become the central concern. No longer does first-hand visual knowledge of the stars and their dates, hours, and positions in the heavens occupy center stage.

Even the old and revered science of astronomy has turned to abstract pursuits. The scholarly theories and learned dissertations of brilliant astronomers have become so profound that they can only be understood by a limited small circle of initiated colleagues.

Beneath the canopy of a dazzling star-covered firmament, both the learned theoretical astronomer and the nationally known writer of astrological columns may not be able to find the star groupings called Gemini, Leo, and Scorpius, or the other nine monthly constellations that inhabit the skies.

Yet today in the technological twentieth century, most persons in the Western Hemisphere know their birthsign. Indeed, *a third of the people in the United States and western Europe believe in astrology* and at least ninety percent are "open-minded," meaning they do not dismiss astrology as outmoded or nonsense, as they would dismiss the idea of a flat earth.[1]

What better way can there be to approach the stars than through the astrological constellations of the Zodiac, familiar to all? But wait! *Zodiac* is also a frequently used astronomical term. In this merry-go-round where *-ology* ends and *-onomy* begins, with one overlapping the other, what is the Zodiac? Let me show you.

* * * * * * * * *

[1] *Science and the Paranormal,* edited by George O. Abell and Barry Singer. New York: Charles Scribner's Sons, 1981, page 72.

Project Zodiac

The Zodiac is often described as "an imaginary belt in the heavens." You will turn imagination into reality and find, even photograph, two important points in the Zodiac that are visible year-round, almost daily. By connecting these key points, you can define the line that forms the center of the Zodiac. This line is called "ecliptic." You will need:

1. a wire coathanger (see "Project Starframe" pages 19–21)
2. today's newspaper
3. a notebook and pencil
4. an alarm clock
5. a camera (optional)

If you are a city dweller, let the flat roof of a high building, or even a skyscraper, serve as the observing platform on your modern counterpart of the historic Babylonian tower. You should be able to see both sunrises and sunsets from such a high vantage point. For those living in the country, the middle of a large field, with unobstructed eastern and western horizons, will serve equally well as a viewing "flatform."

From the weather section of your local newspaper, find out beforehand the exact hours and minutes of today's sunrise and sunset. These times change very little over the course of one week. You should try to plan ahead, also with regard to the forecast of fair-weather days. Check the access to your chosen lookout site in advance to learn how long it will take you to get there, ready to observe. Start with a morning observation. You may need the alarm clock to wake you for such a dawn encounter. Perhaps you will meet the news carrier who daily brings the world to your door, or hear bird songs you never heard before.

The rising sun will announce itself with an eerie first glow in the east. The sky will grow gradually lighter, and whatever stars may be in the sky will soon fade from view. Any moment now, you will be able to anticipate the point on the horizon where sunrise will occur. Note and memorize some distant marker, as well as the exact point where you are standing, so that you can reconstruct the position of today's sunrise again this evening or any time in the future. Now is also the moment to set and prepare the camera if you brought one.

Suddenly there it is: the searing blaze of the exciting first glimpse of the sun. Make a note of the time. How bright our star is! Quickly now; only during the next twenty seconds dare you look at—or photograph—the sunrise spectacle, while most of the solar disc is still hidden below the horizon. Take two vertical photographs (see Diagram A), positioning the bright spot of the sun as nearly in the center of your viewfinder as you can. Do not forget to shoot the frames *vertically* by simply turning the camera 90 degrees, as shown below:

VERTICAL PICTURE

DIAGRAM A

Everything will seem to happen so fast that you may have trouble sorting out the sequence of events for your notes. Here is a checklist of items that should appear in your first astronomical records; write them down immediately while details are fresh in your mind. Not until much later will you realize how valuable such information can become:

1. The correct *date.*
2. The exact *time* of sunrise when *you* first observed it.
3. Your own *location* and precisely where you stood when you first observed it.
4. A verbal *description,* or better yet, a sketch of the sunrise point.
5. The *weather:* clouds or haze, if any.
6. General information: Was the *moon* visible? What shape? (See "The Moon," pages 54–56.)
7. A verbal reconstruction of any *photographs* you may have taken: (a) camera/lens; (b) type of film; (c) f/stop setting(s); (d) length of exposure(s).

HORIZONTAL PICTURE

WARNING: Never *try to look at the sun once it is above and clear of the distant horizon. Serious damage to your eyes can result. Cameras, too, can be permanently disabled when aimed at or near the sun. You may only have twenty seconds for your photography now, but there is always tomorrow. Better safe than sorry. Then, of course, there will be tonight's sunset.*

In the afternoon use your alarm clock once more, to remind you of your twilight appointment with the setting sun. Allow for the extra time it may take to reach your observing site during evening traffic.

Follow all the sunrise procedures again, again being careful not to look at or near the sun, which will still be above the horizon when you arrive at your site. You can safely watch the sun's progress by observing the shade on a nearby wall or on the ground. Remember, as long as there are distinct shadows, the sun remains a hazard to your eyes. Only after they fade and there is a noticeable drop in overall light intensity will it be safe to take two *vertical* photographs. Aim directly at the halo of whatever glow of the sun remains, keeping the "hot spot" centered in the viewfinder as illustrated in Diagram A.

In the evening you will have more time to memorize, or even draw a diagram of, the precise sunset point on the skyline. Once again, note exactly where you stood at sunset. Enter all the observations in your notebook. Just like the ancients, you will be beginning a collection of written records that will become your own most valuable data for the future.

After the sun has set, find an approximation of the nighttime band of the Zodiac. Its position in the sky follows the apparent daylight path of the sun. Now, in the twilight, you can comfortably and safely observe this *seeming* path as it stretches from the sunrise point to the sunset point.

The Zodiac is more than a line. It is a band or a ribbon that has the

ILLUSTRATION 01

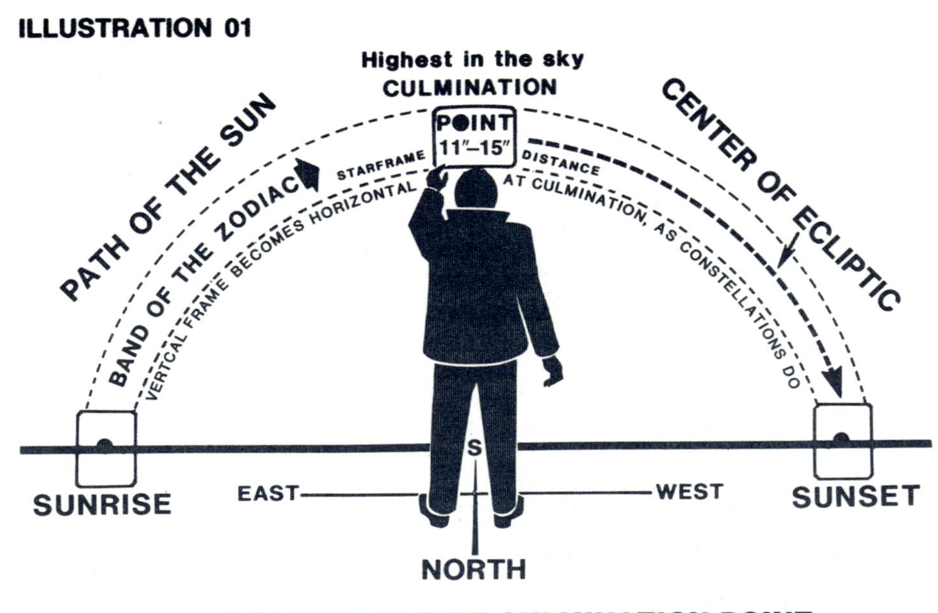

(HIGHEST IN SKY) CULMINATION POINT

apparent path of the sun running along its center. You need a *Starframe* (see page 19) to visualize it. Stand facing due south. Hold the Starframe in your left hand about eleven to fifteen inches from your eyes(s). Outline today's sunrise point on the eastern horizon with the frame held *vertically* (See Diagram A). Now slowly swing the Starframe to where the sun "culminated" and stood highest in the sky at midday today. To find this point see "Project Equinox/Solstice," page 30. Then transfer the Starframe to your right hand and continue to arc it down gradually until it *vertically* frames the sunset point in the west (see illustration 01). When you sweep the Starframe across the sky from sunrise to sunset, its dimensions contain the ecliptic for your day of observation. Note that the ecliptic lies at different elevations, depending on your location on earth and the time of year.

You have just generally encompassed the two halves of the band of the Zodiac and its width in your arcing Starframe. One half of the vast ecliptic circle spans the daylight sky. The second half extends onto the other side of our planet and is invisible below the horizons until night comes. Then, just as the Starframe spanned the sunlit heavens in daylight, the Starframe semicircle at night will complete the wondrous Zodiac halo.

On the following pages, the entire Zodiac is presented in twelve sequential monthly star photographs. Like links in an endless chain, they connect end to end to form a continuous carousel around the sky. As you may notice from your own sunrise and sunset Zodiac observations or photos, each picture frames the same rectangular area that is seen in a Starframe or a standard camera viewfinder. Such rectangles outline and contain what the eye will see when a Starframe is held approximately 15-18 inches from the face. No telescope is needed to match the remarkable observations and discoveries of ancient astrologers. They too used only their eyes, long before lenses (or coathangers) were invented.

Now is a good time to share two other important facts about the Zodiac band. Not only the sun but also our planets and the moon travel within its clearly defined outlines in the sky—and never anywhere else. So if you see a very bright "star" within or near the confines of your Starframe as you swing it from east to west in the morning dawn, in the evening twilight, or especially at night, you may be looking at Jupiter, Saturn, Mars, Venus, or Mercury.

The other reality that intrigues and fascinates is that your own birthsign can also be found in precisely this narrow band of the Zodiac. Whether you believe in horoscopes or never give them a thought, whether you study the influence of the stars and planetary motions upon your life or not, you may wish to find the stars that form your own constellation. Perhaps a so-called astrologer defined your reputed sign of the Zodiac, or found "your" sign by looking it up in an astrological column of a newspaper.

Where in the Zodiac was the sun on the day you were born?

Seeing Is Not Believing

"What's your sign?" is an old and popular question. For many, it serves as a convenient icebreaker in conversation or in meeting a stranger. Others may think that it can create instant insight into the inner traits and secrets of a person. Most Western or English-speaking persons know and can readily name their sunsign in the Zodiac.

What better way to bring the stars to the public than through the medium of what may be their only astronomical connection? Fundamental curiosity presents a wonderful new "astro" opportunity to build a "logical" bridge to the Zodiac. You will easily find "your" stars in the sky by using this manual, together with the coathanger Starframe, which, in outline, you have already seen.

As stated before, your sunsign is determined by the position of the sun in the Zodiac on the date of your birth. Let us say that you were born on the Fourth of July. According to the astrological column in the *Los Angeles Times* (or any other publication), you belong among the "Moonchildren" (June 22–July 21). *Moonchild* is a cosmetic term for the ancient and revered constellation of Cancer, the Crab—*l'Ecrevisse* or *le Cancre* to the French, *Krebs* in German, *il Cancro* or *Granchio* among the Italians; the constellation was known to the ancient Romans and Greeks as *Carcinus.*

Now comes the catch! On the day—or night—of your birth, even your father could not have seen the constellation of the Crab (your mother was busy). Nor can you see your own sunsign on your birthday, today or tonight. The reason is eminently simple: the sun, in the ecliptic, was in your sunsign when you were born, and to observe Zodiac star constellations, it must be night.

The realization that the stars are in the sky even during the daytime may well have been the very first truly scientific discovery. Unwittingly, the ancients complied with three critical demands of science: (1) *observation* (you can duplicate this during sunrise when you gradually lose sight of the fading stars, or at sunset when they reappear), (2) *logical thinking and creative inference* (make comparisons with the thin crescent moon that can be seen at night, is visible in twilight, and may be "discovered" in the daylight sky), and (3) *proof* (any midday total solar eclipse, when the moon occults the sun, will reveal the stars; this proves their constant presence in the sky).

As soon as it gets dark, let us find the nighttime Zodiac. Again, only our Starframe is needed. When we repeat the swing of our hands, arcing the wire outline from the remembered sunrise point in the east to the sunset mark in the west, we will have approximately framed and circumscribed the nighttime Zodiac. The ecliptic is one great circle in the celestial sphere, the apparent track along which the sun travels over the course of a year. It forms an important reference in both the daytime and nighttime sky.

Today we know that the sun does not disappear, is not "swallowed by the sea." Because planet earth is spherical, our moment of sunset in the Americas will be the breathtaking instant of a glorious sunrise in Asia or Africa. Our forebears did not yet know that the world is shaped like a ball. It was believed that earth was flat and, walking or sailing far enough, one would eventually drop off the edge. Observations were often made to fit such preconceived ideas.

Even today, as we see the sun rise in the east and watch its journey across the sky to set in the west, it is easy to side with those who simplistically believed exactly what they saw: a moving sun high above the stationary earth. The Bible, which told of the motion of the sun being stopped "in the midst of heaven,"[1] reinforced the idea of solar motion for all believers. Ancient teachings by learned Greek scholars repeated but could not prove accepted theory that the sun moves through the heavens while the earth

. . . .

[1] Josh. 10:13.

beneath stands still and motionless. Boldly, and with human conceit born from ignorance, we placed ourselves at the center of the universe. We were completely wrong.

No wonder that the writings of Nicolaus Copernicus (1473–1543) were considered "revolutionary" when they first determined that the Earth *revolves* around the sun and that the sun lies at the center of our universe. The concept of the revolution of our planet around the solar center caused a revolution in universal thinking. Those who advocated or believed this bold new idea were accused of heresy by the church. Many were imprisoned; often their tormented bodies were burned alive at the stake.

At first it was difficult to understand, let alone explain and prove, that the apparent motion of the sun in the ecliptic was not real, but only an illusion. It would be hundreds of years before schools could teach real, fundamental truths, which today we may take for granted.

Observing a carousel attendant at an amusement park or a country fair, as a "stand-in" for the sun, can explain the difference between *real* and *apparent* motion. You first notice the young lady in her dazzling orange, brass-buttoned uniform when you purchase your ticket from her at a booth. The next time you spot the orange ticket seller is while you sit waiting on the stationary merry-go-round. She approaches, walking from left (east) to make sure that seat belts are fastened, then strolls away toward the right (west). As you watch her pace around the parked carousel from left to right, her motion is real. Finally, the merry-go-round platform begins to move to the music of the calliope. It turns from west to east, from right to left. You catch sight of the now-familiar bright orange uniform again and again. Just as before, it *seems* to come upon you from the left and disappear on the right. But now the girl's continuing motion is *apparent.* It only *seems* that she moves. You can observe that she is standing quite still, leaning on the ticket booth. Although the girl appears to be moving, she is absolutely stationary.

Galileo's first primitive telescope improved our powers to see. But it was Nicolaus Copernicus, who lived before telescopes were invented, who possessed the greater vision. His remarkable insight changed our world and how we view it, forever.

Project Starframe

You will need: a wire coathanger or coathangers.

It is not uncommon to overhear someone trying to show the night-sky:

"Do you see that faint star about eight inches above the very bright one?"

"No, but I see a star some five feet above it; is that the one you mean?"

Such linear dimensions simply do not work in the heavens. Instead of inches or feet, we need an old and easy standard: angular measure, in degrees. Here the ever-present wire coat hanger can serve a truly "universal" purpose: by bending it into a rectangular Starframe (see illustration 02), we can create an inexpensive degree-measuring tool.

On checking, the faint star above will prove to be exactly 30 degrees above the very bright one. It simply means that if you drew lines from your eye(s) to each of the two stars, they would form an angle of 30 degrees between them. In scientific language, they would *subtend,* or spread out, to the dimension of a Starframe held 15–18 inches from your eye(s). That is 30 degrees (30°) (see illustration 03).

Our wire outline will serve as an invaluable tool at any time of the year, anywhere on earth. It replaces a method based on a haphazard rule of thumb, whereby the human fist was used to "cover" ten degrees, while blocking the view.

The Starframe is ideally suited to help you find and "frame" constellations in the heavens. For clarity, and to do justice to early starwatchers, let us tell their ancient explanation of the starry heavens. For a thousand years it was believed that above the flat earth there was a vast transparent crystal dome to which all of the stars in the sky were attached.

We will be wise to consider this ancient concept together with Copernicus's discovery concerning the apparent motion of the sun. For clarity, we should place our terrestrial merry-go-round in the center of a big transparent plastic "astrodome" that supports all the stars in the heavens. Thus we can combine our modern "revolutionary" knowledge of *apparent* solar motion with correct two thousand-year-old information concerning the starry crystal "bowl in the sky," which was observed to move slowly and gradually, in *real* motion.

Claudius Ptolemaeus (ca. A.D. 90–168), known as Ptolemy, taught that all the stars in the sky revolved around the earth once each year, from east to west.

To complete the picture, let us seat our orange-uniformed attendant (the sun) high in the bleachers, close to the stars in the transparent astrodome. (She is a star, but does not know it yet.) Here is the scenario:

Our earth merry-go-round will make its fast *daily* turns, with the orange sun high in the balcony *appearing and disappearing,* seeming to rise and set 365 times in the course of one year. Over the same period of time, the starry crystal astrodome will make one complete, real, and slow *annual* turn around the earth, in the same direction as the apparent motion of the sun.

Thus we live on a fast-spinning terrestrial merry-go-round, beneath a slowly turning celestial carousel. When you think about it for a little while, you will have discovered cosmic truths that took humankind millennia to unravel.

ILLUSTRATION 02

In order to make our Starframe into an accurate and scientific instrument, we need maintain only one standard measurement: the 15–18-inch distance from the eye to the wire Starframe outline. This can be easily standardized, even in the darkness, without any measuring at all.

Prepare a short piece of string to serve as a permanent Starframe distance gauge. You only need attach a paper clip to one end of the string and tie a Life Saver candy (any flavor) to the other. Measure the overall distance of the gauge so that it is 15–18 inches *from end to end.* Snap the paper clip over the handle of the Starframe, then hold the Life Saver candy in your mouth (see illustration 03). You can also safety-pin it to your lapel, or use a clothespin.

The basic wire Starframe will serve as your permanent celestial viewfinder. Since 30 degrees is the height of the frame, 10 degrees would be one-third of it, etc. You may, in fact, want to compare the area to the field of view you can see through any camera viewfinder of a subject on earth. Try a terrestrial landscape. This will logically make you want to try your hand at star photography. It's easy. See the chapter "Shooting Shooting Stars" (pages 68–70).

When you stretch some transparent acetate kitchen wrap over your basic wire Starframe, you can convert it into a veritable window to the sky. This will be explained in the chapter "Project Stellaphane" (pages 24–26).

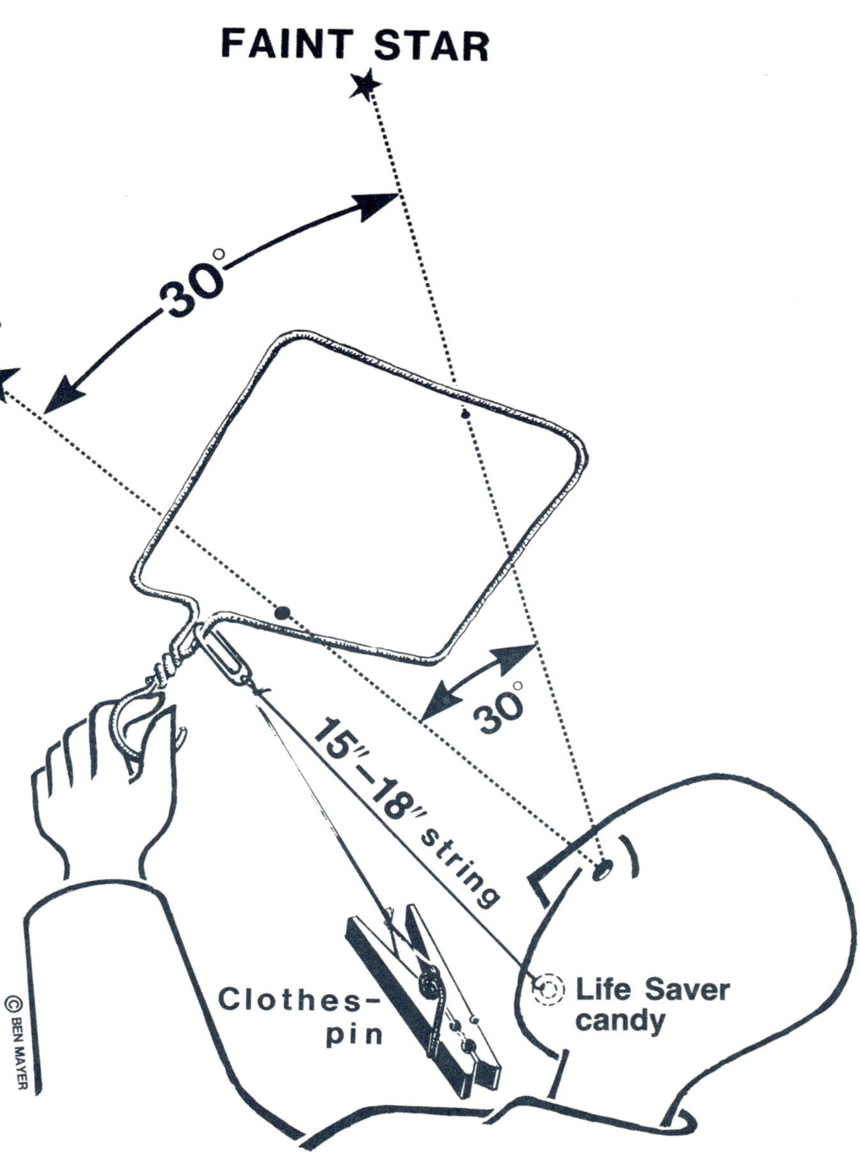

ILLUSTRATION 03

The Celestial Carousel

Starfields were named at about the time when Babylonians began to keep their earliest records. Observers made cakes of fine clay, which they impressed with wedge-shaped chisels. Afterwards, such tablets were dried hard in the hot sun, or even fired in kilns, to give us *cuneiform* writings, which we can decipher today. Thus, we have information concerning their observations—even earliest sightings of an object that we now know as Halley's Comet. That is how almanacs were born. Calendars too were taken directly from observations of the stars, planets, and moon.

It is believed that in archaic times there were only six zodiacal signs: Taurus, Cancer, Virgo, Scorpius, Capricorn, and Pisces. The sight of twelve full moons (months) before a star cycle repeated itself led to the division of the six original signs into the twelve we know today to create a solar year. Gemini, Leo, Libra, Sagittarius, Aquarius, and Aries completed the celestial carousel.

In all cultures, the earliest starwatchers soon related the position of the sun to the seasons. Springtime, the best period for seeding and planting, was always regarded as a beginning in nature, a time of rebirth in the sequence. The cycle was observed to be the period during which the sun apparently, and the celestial star-dome in actual reality, makes one revolution around the earth. In time, the revelation dawned that this period which recurred again and again was the span of one year, by which time itself could be measured.

From cuneiform tablets of the period, we know that the sun (in the crystal astrodome) moved through the stars of Taurus during springtime. Computers allow us to trace back or forward the positions of the sun in relation to the constellations. They confirm that the sun truly passed through the constellation of the Bull in spring between the years 3880 B.C. and 1730 B.C.—modern proof for ancient observations.

No wonder that Taurus was then regarded as "first" among the twelve constellations. In translations and transcriptions from writings of the time, the Zodiac was known as *Pidnu-sha-Shame,* the "furrow of heaven" plowed by the leading bull, five thousand years ago.

By the time Hipparchus (160–120 B.C.), the famous Greek, observed and collected records of the heavens to prepare a star atlas two thousand years ago, the spring sun was no longer to be found in the constellation Taurus. It had moved to the starfield of Aries. By comparing his observations with those of earlier starwatchers, he was able to deduce a very slight, almost imperceptible westward motion of all the stars in the celestial sphere. This is called *precession* and is caused by the gravity pull of the sun and the moon on our planet. It could be described as the turning earth wobbling slightly like a spinning top.

The result of this slow westward movement is that the turning celestial astrodome overhead makes one extra rotation over a period of twenty-six thousand years. This is not noticeable to observers during months or years, but over decades or centuries the effect begins to add up and become apparent even to the naked eye.

If the sun in spring was among the stars of Taurus in Babylonian times five thousand years ago, and among the stars of Aries two thousand years ago at the beginning of the Christian era, it stands to reason that when we observe the sun today it will have moved even further west. "Project Equinox/Solstice" (pages 30–32) will demonstrate how to collect such records.

Hipparchus lived during the flowering of Greece, when strong links were forged with the learning of Mesopotamia and Egypt. Astrologers and astronomers were often one and the same person. They spent much of their time in similar pursuits. Unlike today, astrologers practiced *observational astrology,* whereby stars could help farmers plan their seasons and mariners sailed the seas by their direction. When starwatchers ventured into the world of mathematics or geometry to become astronomers, they were primarily engaged in *observational astronomy.*

Zo- stems from the Greek word for "living being." There is a zoo in the Zodiac. With the exception of Libra, the Scales, all the traditional constellations depict living creatures. It may be fitting that the one starfield that is different is the inanimate scales, weighing the science of astronomy with the art of astrology. Surely there must be a balance between scientific disciplines and emotional perceptions and sensibilities.

If there is a zoo in the Zodiac in the celestial carousel, there surely is a menagerie aboard the terrestrial merry-go-round.

Project Stellaphane

You will need:

1. wire coat hanger or coat hangers: Starframe(s)
2. transparent kitchen wrap
3. typewriter correcting fluid
4. a white opaque marker pen
5. a simple compass

Stella comes from the Latin word for "star," *-phane* from the Greek *phainein,* "to show." Stellaphane Starframes can become the ultimate "window to the sky." Quite simply, they are Starframes with cellophane or acetate plastic kitchen wrap stretched on them. This logical extension of the basic frame viewfinder (see illustration 02) will convert the lowly wire coathanger into the least expensive, most far-reaching astronomical tool. From closet anonymity to Stellar revelations, simple wire coathangers with Stellaphane star tracings can put the heavens into your hands. Faint constellations become accessible for easy discovery.

To create a Stellaphane, we need only "glaze" our Starframe with a transparent windowpane. This can readily be done by cutting a piece of cellophane 10 inches by 12 inches in size, laying the wire rectangle on top of it, folding over the four edges, and taping them down with cellophane tape (see illustration 04).

I have found Saran Wrap[1] to be a superior brand of plastic film to stretch over Starframes and convert them into Stellaphanes. Choosing the 11½-inch-wide roll of transparent film with the cutter bar, pull out and tear off a 14-inch length. Saran Wrap will stick to itself when folded over the frame.

. . . .

[1] Saran Wrap, manufactured by Dow Chemical Company, or a similar product.

To copy the key stars in a constellation onto the plastic, merely lay the Stellaphane on top of any one of the starfields shown. With luminous nontoxic ink,[2] available in hobby or art supply stores, or with typewriter correcting fluid,[3] trace the principal brightest stars in a constellation onto the film. Use a toothpick as an applicator. Dip into the ink, then lightly touch the applicator to the film to transcribe stardots on the transparent sheet. Flow on more ink to match brighter stars, less pigment to copy the fainter ones.

You can hold the Stellaphane in an open warm oven to dry the paint dots while at the same time stretching the Saran Wrap taut as a window. Finally, copy the lines connecting the constellation stars, using a white opaque marker pen.[4]

You will note that the brightest stars form only part of each constellation. Some of these are easy to see and were given Arabic names in olden times, designations that survive to this day. In badly light-polluted areas near big cities, you may have some trouble at first in seeing your constellation. But you will be successful if you start by getting your eyes accustomed to the dark. Once you have found your starfield, you will always be able to rediscover the star grouping.

Don't expect to go out into the night from a brightly lit room and see anything in the sky. Even professional astronomers spend at least twenty minutes in darkness in order for their eyes to become "dark adapted." See "Adapting to the Dark," page 130. Dress

. . . .

[2] Luminous non-toxic Creative Touch manufactured by Palmer Print Products, Troy, Michigan, or a similar product.
[3] White Liquid Paper or a similar product.
[4] DecoColor by Uchida of America Corporation or a similar product.

STELLAPHANE ™
ILLUSTRATION 04
COPYRIGHT 1987 BEN MAYER
PLASTIC WRAP
WHITE FLUID
CUT
CUT
CUT
TRACE LUMINOUS STARS
PAINT WHITE LINES
FOLD OVER
FOLD OVER
SAGITTARIUS
UCHIDA DecoColor opaque white
TOOTHPICK APPLICATOR FOR STAR-DOTS
NON-TOXIC LUMINOUS PAINT

warmly; it may get chilly. Use only a flashlight covered with some red overlay to read this book or to find your way. Place a red cellophane candy wrapper over the bulb of your battery lamp. Such muted light can be used to make the white stardots on the Stellaphane visible in near darkness when you hold it up to lay the stardots over their real counterparts in the sky, as shown in illustration 03.

The best area in which to observe your constellation is the culmination point, and the best time is midnight. Just as the sun *culminates* (stands at its highest) at midday, so the best area for stars is their culmination point, and the time at midnight (standard time; 1:00 A.M. daylight saving time). As the charts show (see pages 10–11), you are not limited to midnight observations. In fact, you can see culminations earlier or later in both date and time. For the sake of simplicity, though, we will employ the midnight culmination time (12:00 midnight, also known as 24:00 hours or 0:00 hours) as our principal time of observation. You should certainly adopt it for your very first searches, and look for the darkest possible observing site.

Stand facing due south. If in doubt, read a compass to confirm direction (use your red flashlight). Hold the Starframe 15–18 inches from your eyes with the string distance gauge you have prepared. Then seek out the brightest two or three stars at the height and time indicated. To "activate" the glow of the luminous ink on Stellaphane Starframes, have a fairly large cardboard box handy in which you can stash a bright light source. Take care not to shine white light on yourself or others nearby to maintain dark adaptation. Setting off a camera flash attachment *within* the blacked-out "light activator box" produces very bright glowing stardots, in a flash. Close your eyes tightly before triggering the flash and warn others with a "countdown": "Three, Two, One, Flashing!"

Depending on location and conditions, the fainter stars in your constellation may be hard to spot at first. But if you follow the date, the hour, and special suggestions given on the constellation pages, you will be on target. So much so, in fact, that if you point a camera as instructed for the Starframe, you should unquestionably be able to photograph all or most of your constellation stars, because the camera can "collect" starlight. (See "Shooting Shooting Stars," pages 68–70).

You need only seek out two, or a minimum of one, brightest stars to align your horizontal Stellaphane Starframe in the sky. Even those stars may seem faint at first, unless you are mistakenly looking at bright planets that journey near the ecliptic *and only in the Zodiac.* These are easy to identify as the brightest objects to be seen. (Planets, which change their positions, are not shown in the starcharts.) See pages 133–134 for planet position information through the year 2000. Suddenly your starfield, first with its brightest star(s) and then with the fainter ones, will dawn in the Starframe. Your stardots will reveal the overlap over their counterparts in the sky. It will have been merely a matter of a little patience. The stars are there, I promise. They have been there almost since time began.

Now that you know when, where, and how to look for your constellation, all that remains is to ask, "What's your sign?"

What's Your Sign?

You probably know your sunsign, and will have found (on pages 17–18) why you may never have actually seen it in the heavens. "What's Your Sign?" will attempt to remedy this oversight. You are not alone in the dark about when, where, or how to look in the night sky to find "your" celestial region in the Zodiac.

Don't forget, the following periods are the months when zodiacal constellations culminate *in the nightsky at midnight* where you can see them. These are *not* the dates when the starfields are at their highest at midday while the sun appears to journey through the daytime Zodiac. You cannot possibly see stars in such daylight skies. We start conventionally at the beginning of the year, during the holiday season, making summer allowances for daylight savings time, and for constellations which overlap in the sky.

CONSTELLATION	MIDNIGHT CULMINATIONS
Gemini	December–January
Cancer	January–February
Leo	February –March
Virgo	April–May
Libra	May–June
Scorpius	June–July
Sagittarius	July–August
Capricorn	August–September
Aquarius	September–October
Pisces	October–November
Aries	October–November
Taurus	November– December

Starting in December–January may be the conventional method today, but it was not always so. The "new year" has become

Zodiac Sunsign (CONSTELLATION)	Sun in Starfield (CULMINATION AT MIDDAY)	Culmination Dates FOR STARFRAMES AT MIDNIGHT	Astrology Dates FROM THE LOS ANGELES TIMES
Pisces	Mar. 11–Apr. 20	Oct. 1–Nov. 1	Feb. 20–Mar. 20
Aries	Apr. 20–May 17	Oct. 15–Nov. 15	Mar. 21–Apr. 19
Taurus	May 17–Jun. 21	Nov. 15–Dec. 15	Apr. 20–May 20
Gemini	Jun. 21–Jul. 17	Dec. 15–Jan. 15	May 21–Jun. 21
Cancer	Jul. 17–Aug. 10	Jan. 15–Feb. 15	Jun. 22–Jul. 21
Leo	Aug. 10–Sep. 18	Feb. 15–Mar. 15	Jul. 22–Aug. 21
Virgo	Sep. 18–Nov. 1	Apr. 15–May 15*	Aug. 22–Sep. 22
Libra	Nov. 1–Nov. 22	May 1–Jun. 1*	Sep. 23–Oct. 22
Scorpius	Nov. 22–Nov. 30†	Jun. 1–Jul. 1*	Oct. 23–Nov. 21
Sagittarius	Dec. 17†–Jan. 19	Jul. 1–Aug. 1*	Nov. 22–Dec. 21
Capricorn	Jan. 19–Feb. 16	Aug. 1–Sep. 1*	Dec. 22–Jan. 20
Aquarius	Feb. 16–Mar. 11	Aug. 15–Sep. 15*	Jan. 21–Feb. 19

*DATES AND TIMES ADJUSTED FOR DAYLIGHT SAVING TIME.

†Nov. 30–Dec. 17: Sun is in Ophiuchus.

accepted through usage and custom in the Western world. There are other cultures with calendars of their own that differ from ours. But all such chronicles relate to the oldest underlying measurement of time: it is the pace of the sun.

When ancient astrologers observed that the earth makes one complete revolution around the sun over the period of one year, they needed a point of reference for their discovery. Obviously there was a cycle, a series of events that occurred again and again. Springtime was accepted as the starting event; nature's rebirth was hailed as the renewal time. But just exactly *when* was the beginning of spring?

For an event in nature to be remembered, even over the period of one year, days had to be counted and records needed to be accurately kept. For observations to be proven over the span of several years, almanacs had to be stored, studied, and compared.

Sons drew upon the records of their fathers, grandfathers, and even great-grandfathers. As societies developed, astrologers, often wise men or leaders, grew in knowledge, esteem, and social position. Scribes or poets recorded their findings. It is to such ancestors that we owe our basic knowledge and the information that five thousand years ago, spring arrived when the sun was in the constellation of Taurus.

"The gleaming Bull opens the year with golden horns," reports an ancient poet. Greek astrology and early astronomical reports tell that the sun was hosted by the constellation Aries, the Ram, during springtime at the beginning of the Christian era. This allowed Hipparchus to discover *precession,* which today is called *westward precession of the equinoxes.*

If you view the sky anytime in spring this century and through the year A.D. 2600, you will be able to observe for yourself that the sun will be in the March–April skies in the constellation of Pisces, the Fishes. This is astrologically and astronomically true and can be verified simply by "observational astrology" during eclipses of the sun.

Because we know that the sun in springtime was in Taurus five thousand years ago, had migrated to Aries two thousand years ago, and is today in the constellation Pisces, anyone can easily predict that the sun will migrate even further westward. The sun will dwell in the constellation of Aquarius next. That is "the age of Aquarius," an astronomical change measured in millennia—in "Genesis seconds." The change is brought about by the fact that the equinoxes migrate slowly westward over the ages, which is caused by the pull of sun and moon upon earth.

As for ourselves, only one fundamental aspect may affect some of us immediately: it is the order of the dates given in astrological charts for the zodiacal constellations and their sequence. They can be found in newspapers or in learned works. Most are wrong. Here is the correct Starframe order, which tells *when the sun is actually in the Zodiac constellations:*

CONSTELLATION	**DAYLIGHT CULMINATIONS**
Pisces	**March–April**
Aries	**April–May**
Taurus	**May–June**
Gemini	**June–July**
Cancer	**July–August**
Leo	**August–September**
Virgo	**September–October**
Libra	**November**
Scorpius	**November–December**
Sagittarius	**December–January**
Capricorn	**January–February**
Aquarius	**February–March**

Now may be the correct time to ask, "What, really, is your sign?"

Project Equinox/Solstice

You will need:

1. access to a freestanding flagpole or power pole
2. calendar (with dates for at least the current year and the next)
3. an alarm clock
4. a thick black felt marker (waterproof)
5. a spray can or long (6-inch) nails (optional)

An equinox is not a living creature, although it dwells on the ecliptic, right in the center of the Zodiac. Many words connected with the study of the stars describe both a "where" and a "when." Just like *sunrise* and *sunset, culmination* and *midday, solstice* and *equinox* mark both moments in time *and* places in space when and where the sun can be found.

The name tells all: *equi-,* from the Latin word for "equal," and *nox,* the Latin word for "night." Equinoxes (there are two, one in spring and the other in autumn) occur when nights and days are exactly equal in length.

The term *solstice* hails from *sol* for "sun" and another Latin word *status,* meaning "having come to a stop." (Again, there are two solstices, one in midsummer and another in midwinter.) Solstices occur when the sun stands highest in the sky in summer, or lowest in the heavens in winter, to give us the longest and shortest days in the year.

Because the earth is tilted in space, the sun appears to spend one half of the year slightly above the celestial equator, then another six months just below it. The "celestial equator" forms an imaginary circle in the sky that girdles the earth and extends endlessly outward from our equator (see Diagram B).

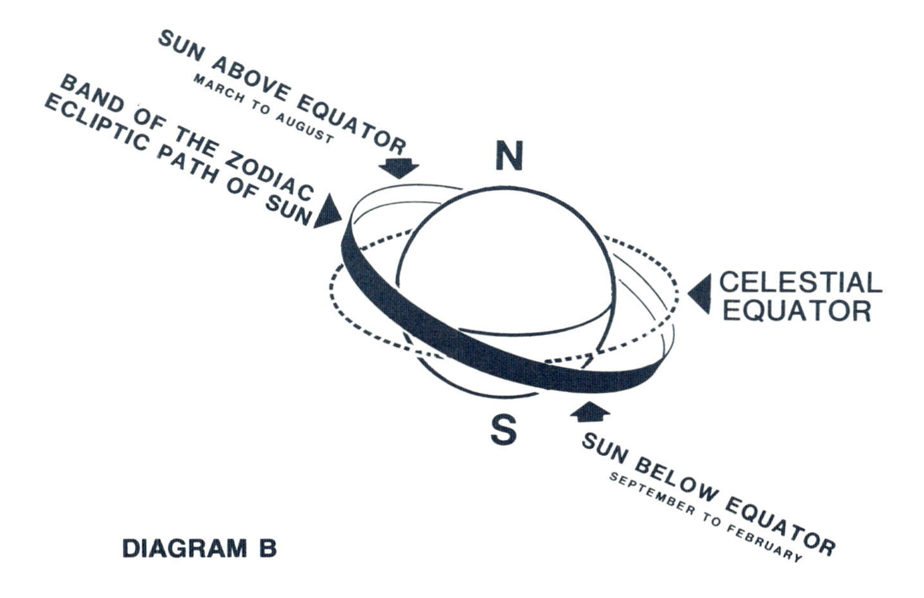

DIAGRAM B

The time of the spring equinox is on the precise day when the sun returns from its Southern Hemisphere passage to the northern skies. The day when the sun crosses the equator marks the beginning of spring. The place of the spring equinox is on the apparent ecliptic path of the sun in the sky. Both time and place are called the *vernal (spring) equinox.*

How could the primitive ancients find the days of the equinoxes? By watching the fiery sun *through its harmless shadows* and counting days, they began their discovery of time. Above all, by diligently recording observations accurately and tirelessly, they invented the earliest calendars. You can yet recreate the romance of one of the oldest of experiments. It was performed by prehistoric Eastern cultures and among obscure American peoples. The faithful sun can be your eternal link to dwellers on the banks of the Nile, or to the sacrificial altars of long-forgotten ancestors.

Any vertical pole can serve as a *gnomon,* or pointer. Such an indicator will, by the position or length of its shadow on the ground, serve to reveal the location of the sun in the sky. Let any free-standing flagpole, telephone pole, or power pole play the counterpart role of the most ancient and reliable shadow pointer to the sun.

You can perform part of Project Equinox/Solstice at any time of the year. If it is not cloudy, tomorrow may be a good day. (See also "Project Zodiac," pages 14–16.) This is an exercise that must be done when the sun stands highest in the sky, at high noon standard time; (1:00 P.M. daylight saving time), or as close to it as possible. Set your alarm clock a little ahead of the noon hour and prepare to stand near the shadow of your chosen gnomon (pointer pole).

For starters, you may wish to determine the hour of high noon by observing the shadow line and determining just when it points due geographic north. Don't forget, the ancients had no compasses. For them, the north-south line of direction lay exactly perpendicular to and in the center of the line connecting sunrise and sunset, which you have already noted. Often, long sticks were used instead of flagpoles as sun pointers. The importance of Stonehenge or its monoliths will immediately become clear when we think of them as pointer stones between which the sun could be sighted on distant horizons. This permitted the simplest finding of directions (and dates).

We will not even be "cheating" if we mark in our calendar the dates of March 16–26, during which the spring equinox is known to occur, or the period between September 16 and September 26, which is when the autumn equinox comes to pass. We will be using the modern calendar, based on the work of diligent observers many ages ago, and we will thus be walking in their shadows.

Let us also mark the summer and winter solstices and when they fall due. Enter the time spans June 16–26 and December 16–26. Among these days, there should at least be one when the sun will be free of clouds or fog at midday. With these days marked for observation, you will never be more than three moons away from

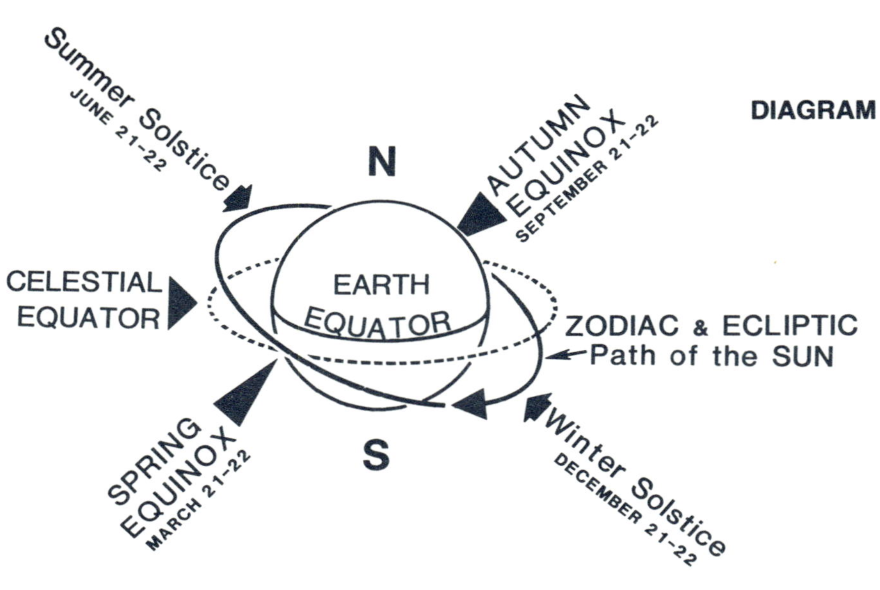

DIAGRAM C

an opportunity to conduct a "hands-on" equinox or solstice project (see Diagram C).

The procedure for Project Equinox/Solstice is the same in all cases. You want to measure the length of the shadowline that is being cast by the pole on the ground. For a record, and to remind you in the future, enter your observations *(data)* below:

> The following are the measured lengths of the shadowline from the base of the ______________ pole, flagpole, power-pole (check one) at ______________ ______________ (give address and description). Times are given in local standard time and in universal standard time (phone your nearest observatory or planetarium for this important information; ask for Greenwich or universal time).

DATE	OBSERVATION	LOCAL TIME	UNIVERSAL STANDARD TIME	SHADOW LINE LENGTH
____	spring equinox	__hrs__mins	__hrs__mins	______
____	summer solstice	__hrs__mins	__hrs__mins	______
____	autumn equinox	__hrs__mins	__hrs__mins	______
____	winter solstice	__hrs__mins	__hrs__mins	______

Take several measurements, which is the scientific way to conduct an experiment, to avoid errors. Measure in feet and inches or in meters and centimeters. You may wish to mark the end of the shadow on the ground with your felt pen (or even with the paint spray can) if the conditions and surface allow. Where soft soil is involved, you can drive the long nails into the ground as permanent markers.

The most important aspect of engaging in Project Equinox/Solstice is that it will inevitably set you to thinking. As the Greek word *gnōmōn,* which means "interpreter," suggests, you will have to interpret your data, beginning with the actual position of the sun. You will enjoy drawing correct conclusions as to the place where the sun stands in the sky at the time you make your observations.

Quite clearly, the sun is above the far side of the pole opposite the shadowline, which will point due north. At noon, this places the sun in the southern part of the sky. The shorter the shadowline during the summer solstice, the higher in the sky is the position of the sun. Conversely, the longer the shadowline around the winter solstice, the lower the sun stands in the heavens. At the time of the equinoxes, the length of the shadow will be exactly at the halfway point. You should be able to figure out a third value once you have either of the other two measurements in hand. That is how scientists work, by *extrapolation.*

Project Equinox/Solstice may make you realize how much we owe long-forgotten ancestors. It is on the work of these remarkable anonymous forebears, in all parts of our globe, that knowledge is based. Over time, they built larger and more accurate measuring tools so that their knowledge increased, as did our own. But finally, the most remarkable of all instruments was the extraordinary human brain. The projects in these pages are merely gnomons, interpreters of a wonderful past and pointers to a future filled with wonder.

The Astro-Ology/Onomy Connection

It was January when I presented a paper on video blink comparison (see "The Blinking Rabbit Discovery," pages 84–86) to the 169th meeting of the American Astronomical Society in Pasadena. I feel honored to belong to the A.A.S., which mainly consists of professional astronomers, a veritable Who's Who among members of this occupation. I had been accepted into the ranks because of observations and photographic patrol work I am performing as an amateur astronomer.

The setting of the evening banquet was auspicious. It was held in the prestigious Athenaeum faculty club at Caltech beneath the Shadow of Mount Wilson where Edwin Hubble had toiled to shed brilliant new light on the stars in our universe. I was seated among credentialed Ph.D.'s, astronomers, physicists, and deep-space researchers. Conversation had turned to the need for a greater enrollment by the public in the Astronomical Society of the Pacific (A.S.P.), which is open to anyone anywhere who loves the stars, cosmologists and amateur or armchair astronomers alike.[1]

When I suggested to the group at our table, which included the president of the Astronomical Society of the Pacific along with its executive director and one A.S.P. board member, that I felt I knew a way to increase interest in the prestigious one-hundred-year-old organization, my words met with some attention. But it was my mentioning the word *astrology* that brought all conversation to a halt. I had dared use, in a serious context, a word that was never spoken in such hallowed halls except in jest. Here Nobel laureates (even the great Albert Einstein himself) had walked the corridors, and serene paintings and photographs of esteemed scientists adorned the paneled walls.

"We should forge a bridge in the minds of the public," I suggested, "between universal interest in the heavens and the stars through the one viable connection which can unite them all: the Zodiac, and what might be called observational astrology. After all, astronomers as well as the general public have heard about, or know, the Zodiac. Most people just do not know where to find it." Some thought I was jesting and may have dismissed my concept outline. The dessert was being served in silence to the assembled guests. I felt that some instant clarification was needed. There was nothing to lose.

"Sir," I called out to the waiter for all to hear, "what's your sign?"

Instantly the reply came back: "Gemini!"

"Have you ever seen the stars of Gemini, the Twins, in the sky?"

"No, never."

Here was my opportunity. "Would you mind coming with me for a moment?" I asked as I rose to escort the man from the historic building into the illuminated parking lot outside. The light pollution was appalling. There was a half-moon.

. . . .

[1] For membership information, write to Astronomical Society of the Pacific, 1290 24th Avenue, San Francisco, California 94122.

"This is the moon," I intoned, pointing while I established my directions—the waiter may have doubted my sanity at this moment—"and that bright object over there is not a star; it is the planet Jupiter. Just above it, the reddish object is the planet Mars." Now I had the waiter's full attention. To him, quite obviously I was one of the learned men of science assembled at the Athenaeum—a little touched perhaps, but informed. Then came the chance for my grandstand play.

"Do you see the pair of bright stars almost directly overhead?" I asked, pointing near the zenith.

"Yes," he said.

"Those two stars are Castor and Pollux, the brightest pair in the constellation of Gemini, the Twins," I continued, and then indicated the much fainter companion stars that barely hinted at the familiar twin stick figures.

When I returned to the table, I was able to recount how even from the light-polluted parking lot in the Caltech compound I had been able to demonstrate one lunar, two planetary, and several stellar objects in the constellation of Gemini, to the interest and delight of our waiter.

It had all happened so fast that now in the immediate aftermath it seemed possible that it was my astronomer friends who may have failed to grasp my intentions. If I did not immediately convince the assembled company of my purpose, at least I felt that I was opening a feasible vista to a new affinity between two related but conflicting doctrines.

For myself, I well remember an important lesson learned that night, beyond the obvious need for compromise between astronomy and observational astrology, to the benefit of both: Even if you are not familiar with the fainter stars in constellations, but know when and where to look, you can begin to find your way in the starry heavens. All you need is an awareness of direction, knowledge of the date and time, and one or two bright "anchor" stars such as Castor and Pollux. These two were easily visible even under the glare of bright lights during that night in the parking lot of the Athenaeum, not far from the world-famous Jet Propulsion Laboratory in Pasadena.

All you need to find the twelve Zodiac regions are:

1. the appropriate constellation Stellaphane Starframe
2. your Starframe distance measuring gauge
3. a flashlight covered with red cellophane or cloth, a red bottle cap, or a kraft paper sack
4. a compass
5. a lightproof cardboard box to "activate" the luminous stardots on your Stellaphane Starframe (use white light or any camera flash)
6. an alarm clock set to ring well before the preferred observation time
7. warm clothes and perhaps extra socks
8. a pair of binoculars (optional)
9. a camera and tripod (optional)

Project Gemini

THE GREEK ALPHABET

α	ALPHA	η	ETA	ν	NU	τ	TAU
β	BETA	θ	THETA	ξ	XI	υ	UPSILON
γ	GAMMA	ι	IOTA	ο	OMICRON	φ	PHI
δ	DELTA	κ	KAPPA	π	PI	χ	CHI
ε	EPSILON	λ	LAMBDA	ρ	RHO	ψ	PSI
ζ	ZETA	μ	MU	σ	SIGMA	ω	OMEGA

You too can best start the new year by observing Gemini at midnight on January 1. (Please note: by looking in the index you can find any of the other eleven Zodiac projects. This will allow you to start your quest at any time of the year.) On the fifteenth of January it will stand at its highest, nearly overhead (to the south) at 23:00 hours (or 11:00 P.M.). On the following page are the best times and dates for a six-month period.

For post-midnight and early morning observations, set your alarm clock to ring well before the appointed hour. Dress warmly and avoid white light. Go to your observation site ahead of time to allow your eyes to get accustomed to the darkness. The ease with which you will be able to find bright Castor and Pollux will make Gemini into an ideal first constellation to observe. You will obtain invaluable understanding of the sky and angular distances. It is impossible to explain in words the critical usefulness of the Stellaphane Starframe for gaining insight into the nominal 5 degrees that separate the Alpha (**α**) and Beta (**β**) stars in Gemini, as Castor and Pollux are known to astronomers. Have your Stellaphane Starframe distance gauge ready to explore the region for yourself. Start activating your luminous stardots in the light box, taking care not to "spill" any stray light.

You are facing due south, aren't you, so that you can hold the Stellaphane Starframe high in the southern sky as shown in illustration 05? Predictably, Castor and Pollux will be the brightest objects in your viewfinder frame, unless one of the bright major planets is spending some weeks wandering through the confines of your starfield. (For more on planets, see "Half Empty or Half Full?" page 48) Chances are that Alpha (**α**) and Beta (**β**) alone dominate the field in Gemini, so you can start scouting for the

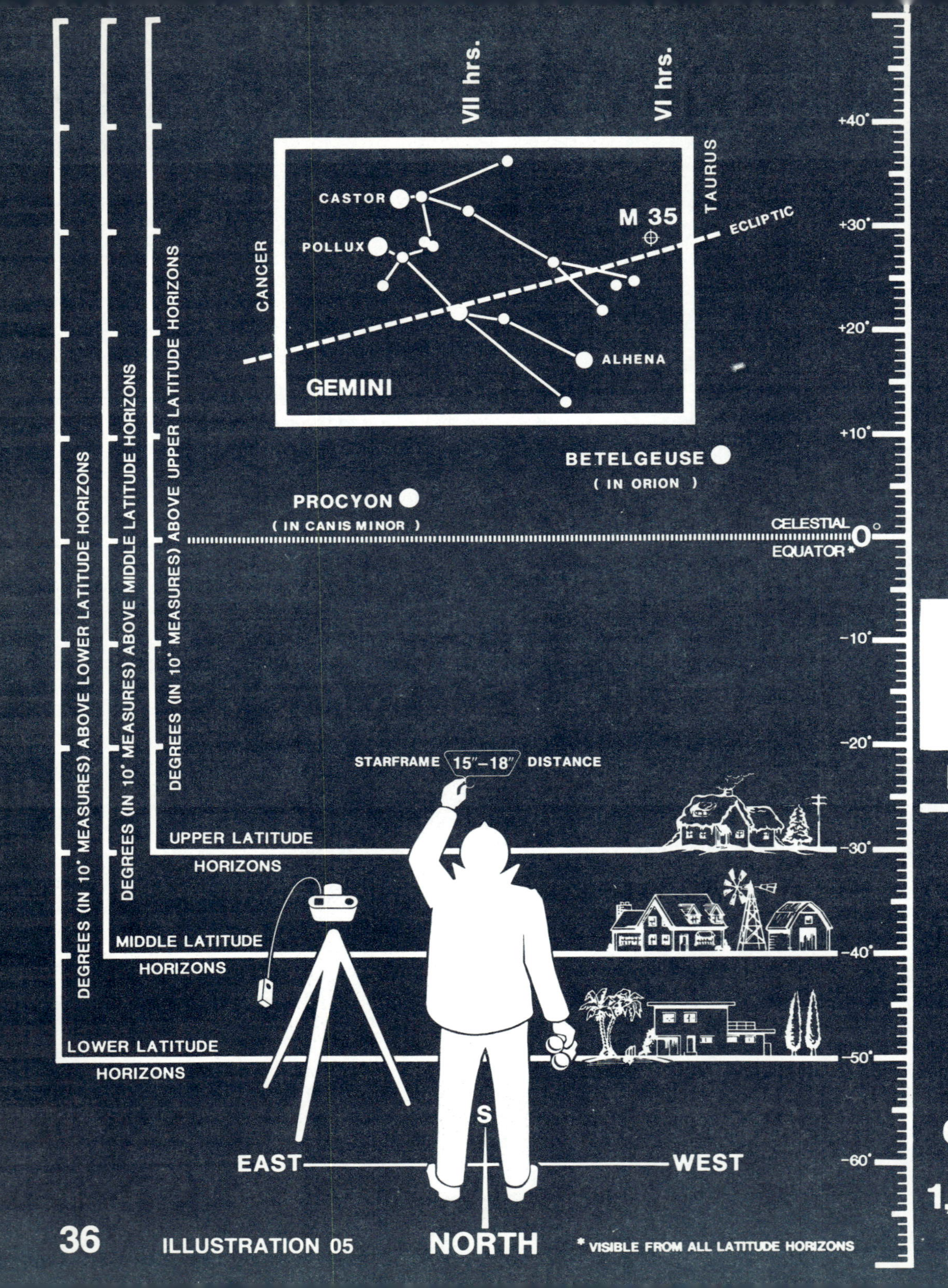

ILLUSTRATION 05

CULMINATIONS OF THE GEMINI STARFIELD
(see illustration on left)

Hold the Starframe 15–18 inches from the eye

October 15-November 1	at 5:00 am	= 05:00 hours
November 1-November 15	at 4:00 am	= 04:00 hours
November 15-December 1	at 3:00 am	= 03:00 hours
December 1-December 15	at 2:00 am	= 02:00 hours
December 15-January 1	at 1:00 am	= 01:00 hours
January 1-January 15	at MIDNIGHT	= 24:00 hours
January 15-February 1	at 11:00 pm	= 23:00 hours
February 1-February 15	at 10:00 pm	= 22:00 hours
February 15-March 1	at 9:00 pm	= 21:00 hours
March 1-March 15	at 8:00 pm	= 20:00 hours
March 15-April 1	at 7:00 pm	= 19:00 hours

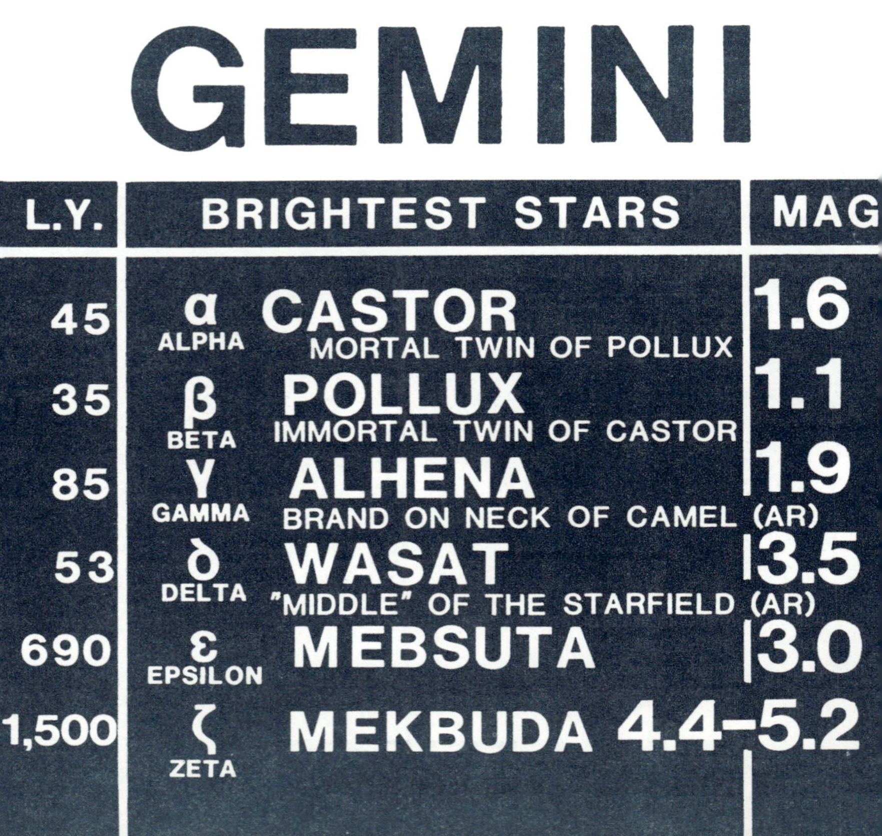

GEMINI

L.Y.	BRIGHTEST STARS	MAG
45	α ALPHA CASTOR MORTAL TWIN OF POLLUX	1.6
35	β BETA POLLUX IMMORTAL TWIN OF CASTOR	1.1
85	γ GAMMA ALHENA BRAND ON NECK OF CAMEL (AR)	1.9
53	δ DELTA WASAT "MIDDLE" OF THE STARFIELD (AR)	3.5
690	ε EPSILON MEBSUTA	3.0
1,500	ζ ZETA MEKBUDA	4.4–5.2

fainter stars that together represent what has long been seen to be a pair of matchstick figures.

It is because of their bright magnitudes that the two key stars in Gemini are so easy to spot. Both Alpha (α) and Beta (β) are first-magnitude stars. The Gamma (γ) star, known as Alhena, is near second magnitude. It will help you find the overall length of one of the two figures of the Twins. All other Gemini stars are at third magnitude or fainter, which will pose no problem under good dark skies where the naked eye can see stars to magnitude six. Where there is much light pollution, you may have to search for these fainter suns. After a little time, and as you get more accustomed to the darkness, such fainter stars may seem to suddenly materialize in your Starframe.

Whether you observe from the hills of Vermont or stand in the Mojave Desert, you will inevitably forge a bond with antiquity and with ancient peoples who knew the stars and their lore extremely well. The variable star R in Gemini changes in brightness from magnitude 6.0 to invisibility at magnitude 14.0. Other variables, S and T, are also marked. They may show in some photographs and be absent in others. There are many variables in the Zodiac and in the sky overall. See the reference to variable star observations in "Project Leo," pages 51–53. You may want to keep an eye on these regular beacons or some of their irregular counterparts.

If you observe from a dark sky area and have a pair of binoculars available to you, the areas around Castor & Pollux and nearby as shown in the starchart deserve closer scrutiny. The field of view of a standard pair of binoculars is about 6–8 degrees in diameter. It will contain both Alpha (α) and Beta (β) geminorum together. One interesting object shown is the *galactic cluster* numbered M35 by a French astronomer who first observed it in August 1764 (see illustration 05). With a medium-power telescope, over a hundred stars can be distinguished in this grouping. Such wonders hint at the incredible treasures that await us in the night sky, not only in the Zodiac, but anywhere we may focus our eyes.[1]

The *M* before the number 35 commemorates Charles Messier (1730–1817), who first compiled a list of interesting objects in the sky. Most of the starfields shown in this book contain one or several such Messier objects. Try to observe them with binoculars.

• • • • • • • • •

[1] For information on additional bright and exciting starfields beyond the band of the Zodiac, and much more information on variable stars see Mayer, *Starwatch*. New York: Perigee, 1984. (See coupon page 143.)

AIM CAMERA AT ⊕ TARGET BETWEEN TWINS

GEMINI

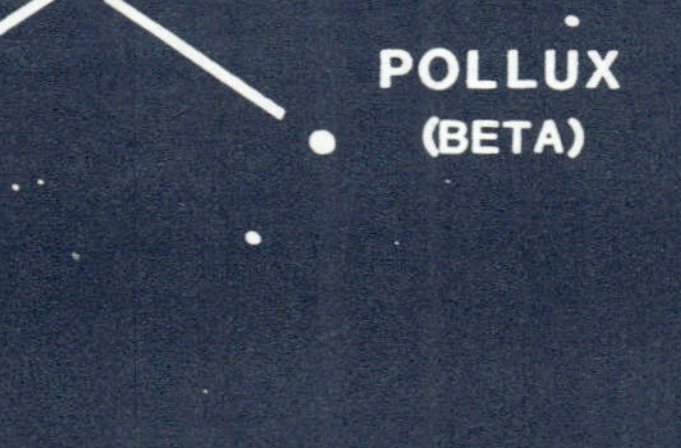

STANDARD 50 MM LENS

ALIGN WITH CASTOR AND POLLUX

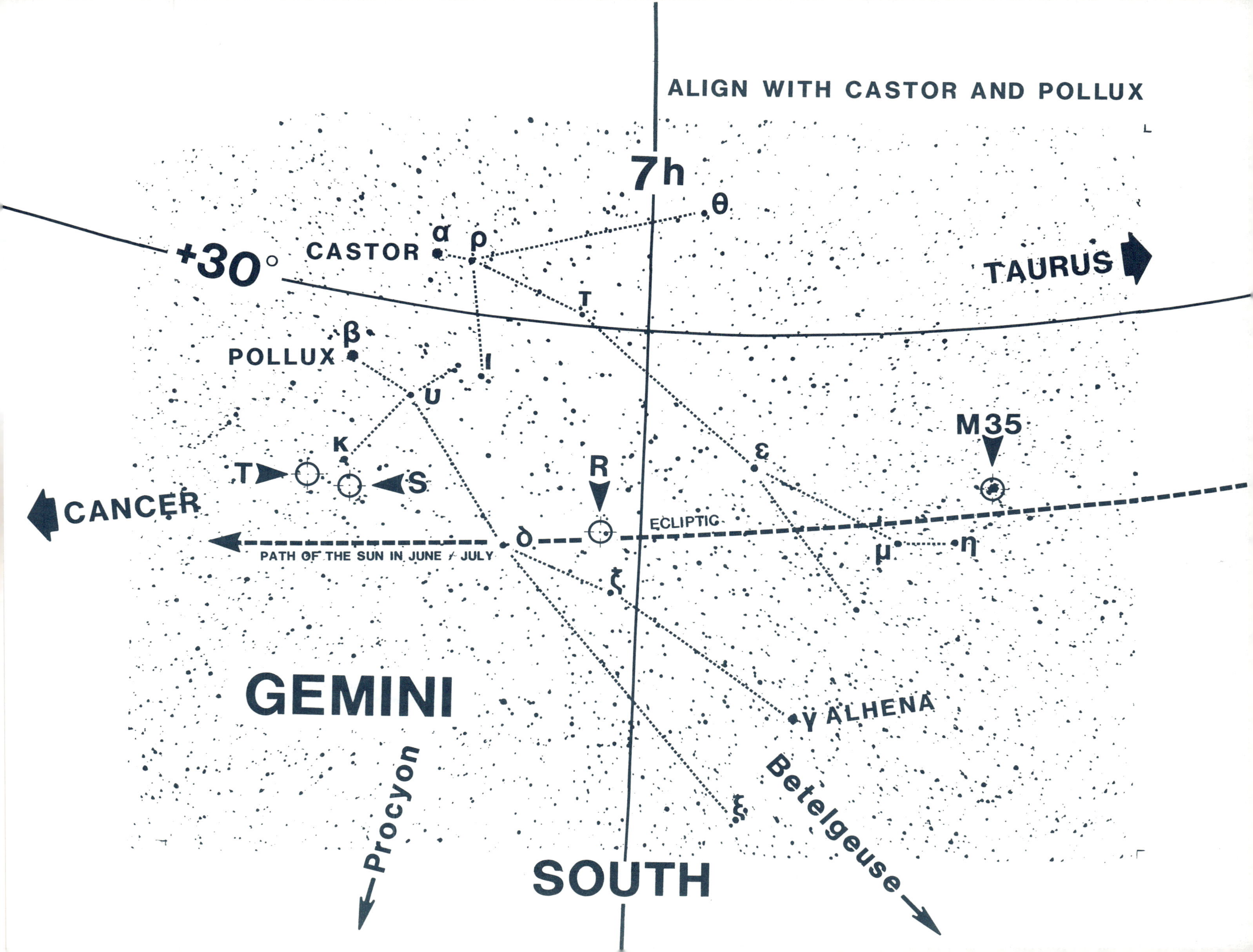

ALIGN WITH CASTOR AND POLLUX

7h

θ

+30°

α

ρ

CASTOR

TAURUS

τ

β

POLLUX

ι

υ

M35

κ

ε

R

T

S

CANCER

ECLIPTIC

δ

μ

η

PATH OF THE SUN IN JUNE / JULY

ζ

GEMINI

γ ALHENA

Procyon

Betelgeuse

ξ

SOUTH

What Time Is It?

The next time someone asks you, "What time is it?" your response could well be the question, "What time is it . . . *where*?"

Within fifty-nine minutes and fifty-nine seconds it will be twelve o'clock noon in some time zone on earth. Similarly, at the opposite point on the globe it will be midnight, or 24:00 hours.

We modern walkers-on-the-moon have almost forgotten those who believed that the earth was flat. We must not forget their starry crystal dome in the heavens above, but let us replace it with a transparent spherical bubble that surrounds our ball-shaped earth. This will serve our purpose even better, especially if we make the bubble of inflatable material so that we can blow it up to endless size. In this manner, the stars that are painted on it can be visualized all around at varying light-year distances, far away from our planet.

Place earth, with the band of the Zodiac inside this giant inflated celestial bubble, with the equator at a slight angle to the band of the Zodiac as shown (see illustration 06). As illustrated, it has long been possible to tell positions on earth in the *north-south* direction of the ladder of latitude. The equator (and the sky equator beyond it) are at the zero position. Northern latitudes are shown in plus degrees of angle as measured from the center of our earth. They go from 0 degrees to +10 degrees, +20 degrees, +30 degrees, +40 degrees, up to the North Pole, which lies at +90 degrees. The north celestial pole (N.C.P.) is above the earth's North Pole, also at +90 degrees; southern latitudes are said to be at minus degrees at 0 degrees −10 degrees, −20 degrees, −30 degrees, all the way to −90 degrees marking the South Pole. It is easy to tell latitudes from longitudes (see below) when you think of the latitudes as the rungs of a ladder where they are on top of or below the equator.

Until three hundred years ago, we had no way to determine *east-west* positions of longitude. It was the need of Britain's Royal Navy that resulted in the invention of accurate portable clocks to permit time- and place-keeping on sea-tossed ships.

Twenty-four hours of *right ascension* (R.A.) were established concerning the order in which the stars rise. These related to the "when" in time and the "where" in space in the east–west direction of longitude. We have long defined the zero position in the sky as the moment of the vernal equinox when the sun crosses the equator in spring. The final and fundamental question was where the "zero hour of longitude" should be here on earth.

So-called Royal Astronomers at the Royal Observatory in Greenwich, England, were the first to bridge the vital relationship between the "when" of the equinox in the heavens and the "where" of time and place on our planet. By international treaty, the very line running through the telescope at the Royal Observatory in England was chosen as the *prime meridian,* the zero point in time and in east-west longitude. Time was enshrined "for all time" on the Greenwich zero meridian, from which the globe and its hours would be measured forever.

Depending on where you live, you are either "behind" Greenwich mean time or "ahead" of its time standard. When it is midday in London, it is 7:00 A.M. (*ante meridiem:* before noon) Eastern standard time, 8:00 A.M. Eastern daylight time, in New York. In Los Angeles, it is 4:00 A.M. Pacific standard time, 5:00 A.M. Pacific daylight time, and in summer the sun is just rising. Hawaii is still dark at 1:00 A.M. In Japan it is already "tomorrow."

With the help of a shortwave radio you may enjoy setting an electric clock in your home to accurate Greenwich time, also known as *universal time* or *U.T.* This will make you independent of

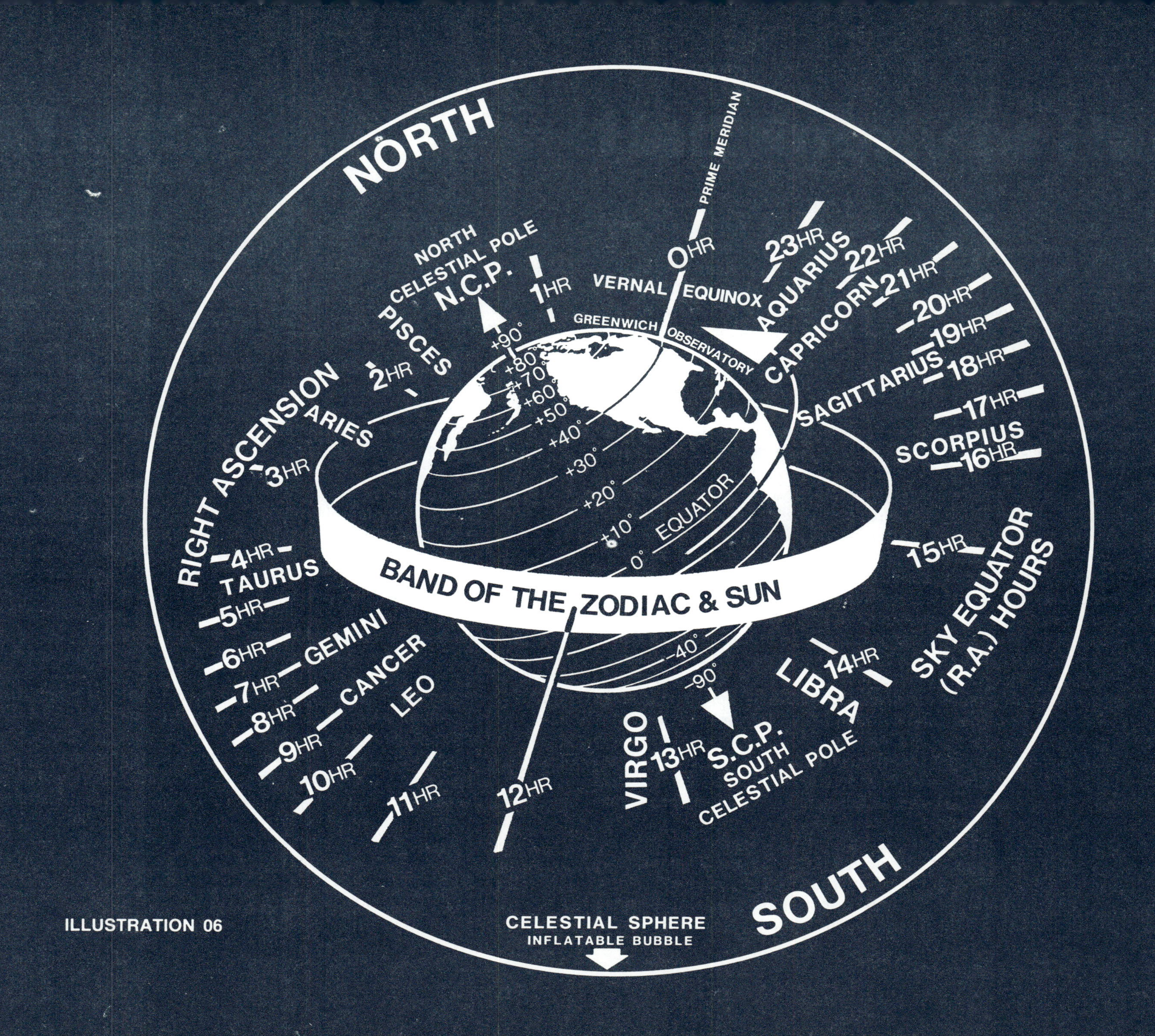

ILLUSTRATION 06

the time zone in which you live, and of the seasonal changes to daylight saving time or standard time. Astronomers everywhere on earth observe this uniting discipline whether they work in the Soviet Union, the United States, Australia, or Africa. You may want to enter records in your log both in local time and in U.T. This will give your observations and any discoveries you make the added weight of scientifically correct timing. Since time is coordinated by the finest international observatories and is ultimately guided by the heavens, you will constantly be "in step with the stars."

In "Project Starframe" (pages 19–21), we found that the vertical (latitude) dimension of a Starframe is about 30 degrees on its narrow side when held 15–18 inches from the eye. You can visually verify this by aligning the lower edge of the frame with the horizon and then swinging the Starframe vertically up, frame over frame above frame. Three Starframes stacked in this way will take you from the horizon to the zenith, the point vertically above your head. The zenith point is at an angle of 30 degrees plus 30 degrees plus 30 degrees, equaling +90 degrees from the horizon.

To confirm the wire coathanger as the ultimate low-cost astronomical tool, you can also quickly establish that its width corresponds to two *R.A. hours.* These are the measures astronomers call hours of right ascension (see above). A quick check will prove that when held at the 15–18-inch Starframe distance, twelve Starframes side by side will circle the entire horizon from south around all points of the compass and back to south again. Quite fittingly, this makes the heavens into a twenty-four-hour, year-round clock dial.

It will be easy to pinpoint the Zodiac constellations pictured in this book. You only need follow the given times and dates to aim yourself in the right direction. All Zodiac observations must be made with the Starframe pointing due south, your back to the north. (Verify your direction with a red flashlight and a compass). Please follow the observation times on pages 10–11 accurately as well as the dates, as far as weather and the moon permit. You will not have to turn from your north-south direction: the constellations and their stars will come into sight one after the other, from east to west, over the course of a year. A range of observing times is offered, the earlier ones favoring observations in the company of youngsters. You will find that the later midnight or 2:00 A.M. times may give you better seeing conditions near cities, when lights are turned off. They will also give you the opportunity to view different constellations over the course of a night if you allow a minimum of two hours between observations. There are seventy-six additional constellations in the sky that are not part of the Zodiac but that can be found with Stellaphanes traced from any large-scale sky atlas.

Do not be discouraged, even if at first you need extra time and patience to find the starfield of your choice. You may have trouble with light pollution. However, there is one redeeming feature to this modern problem that has beset our cities and their surroundings. I have gone so far as to call it "benign light pollution." Although the fainter stars may be harder to detect at first under suburban conditions, you *will* be able to find and see them. You really need only one star to "lock" your tracing to a starfield. Two stars will give you direction *and* scale. After that you are home free, especially after your eyes have become better accustomed to darkness.

Nothing can equal the dazzling beauty of a dark, country nightsky, and from time to time you should attempt to make observations from the darkest site possible. But be prepared when you go out for the first time to a perfect stargazer's sky. You will need a Stellaphane to help you back into the Zodiac among the profusion of stars that awaits. With each new star or galaxy you can spot, your wonder and curiosity will grow until you have fallen under the spell of starlight and the ancient mysteries it holds.

Project Cancer

As always you will need:

1. a prepared (Cancer) Stellaphane Starframe
2. your Starframe distance measuring gauge
3. a compass
4. a red-masked flashlight
5. a lightweight cardboard box to "activate" the luminous stardots on your Stellephane Starframe
6. an alarm clock set to ring well before the selected observation time
7. warm clothes and perhaps extra socks
8. a pair of binoculars (optional)

We have already spoken of names for the constellation Cancer (on page 17) in connection with the euphemism "Moonchildren." When we think of the contrived substitution of a less offensive name for those born under the sign of Cancer, this project chapter should put all moonchildren's concerns to rest. Persons supposedly born under the constellation of the Crab were, in fact, mostly born under the sign of Gemini, which was reviewed in the previous project chapter.

Astronomically—and astrologically—the sun nowadays is in the daylight sky of Cancer between July 17 and August 10. This places the path of the solar disk highest in the midnight sky between January 15 and February 15 for best Cancer pictogram observations from a dark sky site.

On or about April 1, daylight saving time (D.S.T.) begins in most places and clocks are set forward. You may have to make a one-hour adjustment to allow for the longer hours of daylight. If you run your projects on universal time (U.T.) as suggested in "What Time Is It?" (pages 40–42), your sun will rise, set, and march to a different drummer. You will really become a serious astronomer and discover that the hour you may have "lost" in evening darkness becomes a gift of extra observing time before sunup in the morning.

The constellation of Cancer, the Crab, is not easy to find. Therefore, the use of the Stellaphane Starframe in combination with a compass on the dates and times listed above becomes most important in establishing *where* to look for it. In altitude, hold your Starframe due south, with its center approximately 60 degrees (two Starframes) above the southern horizon as illustrated. When the Cancer Stellaphane Starframe is first held 15–18 inches from your eye, virtually nothing may seem to be contained in this region of the viewfinder, unless one or more of the dazzling planets are visiting the starfield of the Crab. Castor and Pollux should still be

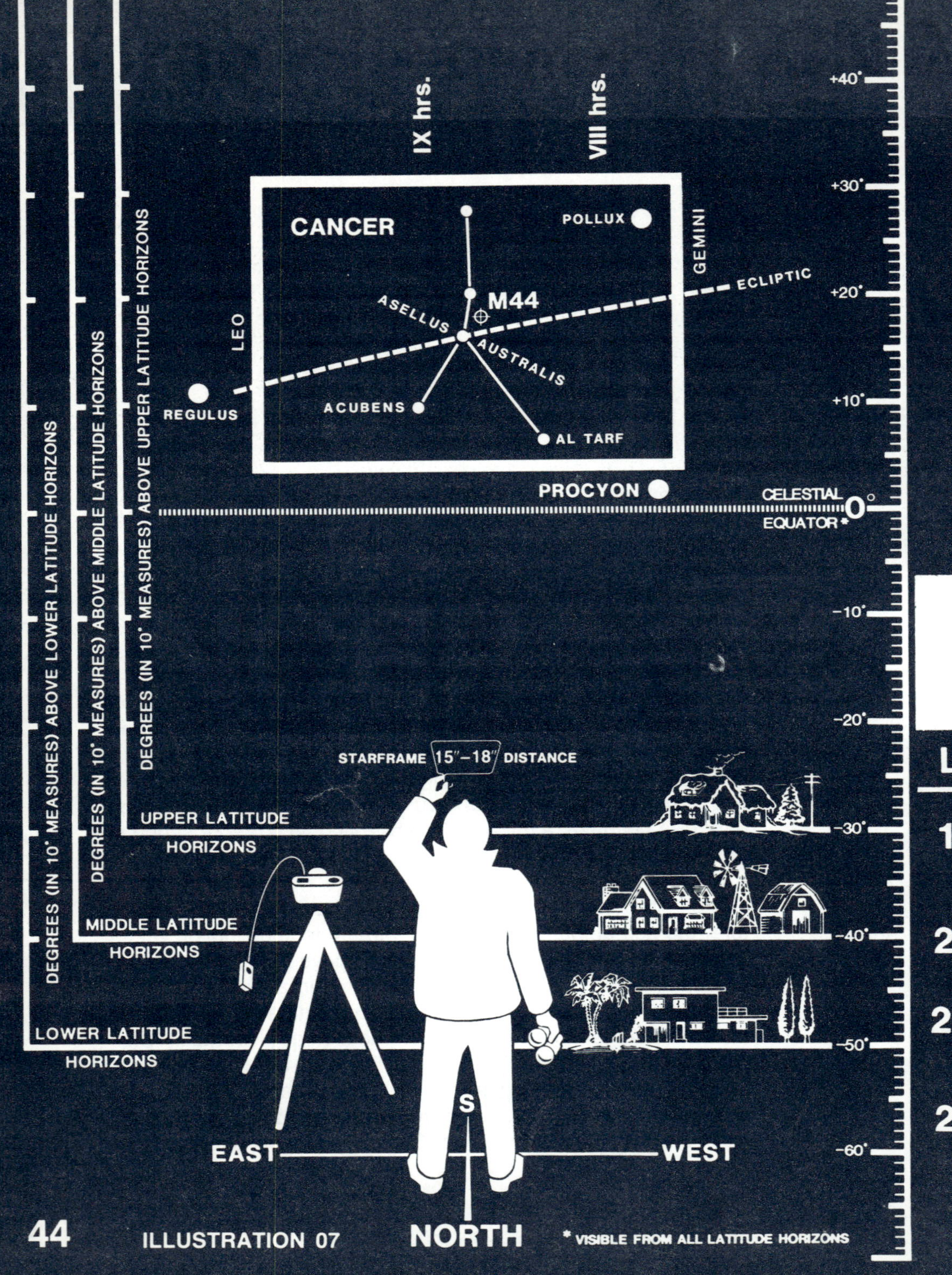

CULMINATIONS OF THE CANCER STARFIELD
(see illustration on left)

Hold the Starframe 15–18 inches from the eye

November 15-December 1	at 5:00 am	=	05:00 hours
December 1-December 15	at 4:00 am	=	04:00 hours
December 15-January 1	at 3:00 am	=	03:00 hours
January 1-January 15	at 2:00 am	=	02:00 hours
January 15-February 1	at 1:00 am	=	01:00 hours
February 1-February 15	at MIDNIGHT	=	24:00 hours
February 15-March 1	at 11:00 pm	=	23:00 hours
March 1-March 15	at 10:00 pm	=	22:00 hours
March 15-April 1	at 9:00 pm	=	21:00 hours
*April 1-April 15	at 9:00 pm	=	21:00 hours
*April 15-May 1	at 8:00 pm	=	20:00 hours
*May 1-May 15	at 7:00 pm	=	19:00 hours

*Time on these dates is adjusted for daylight saving time.

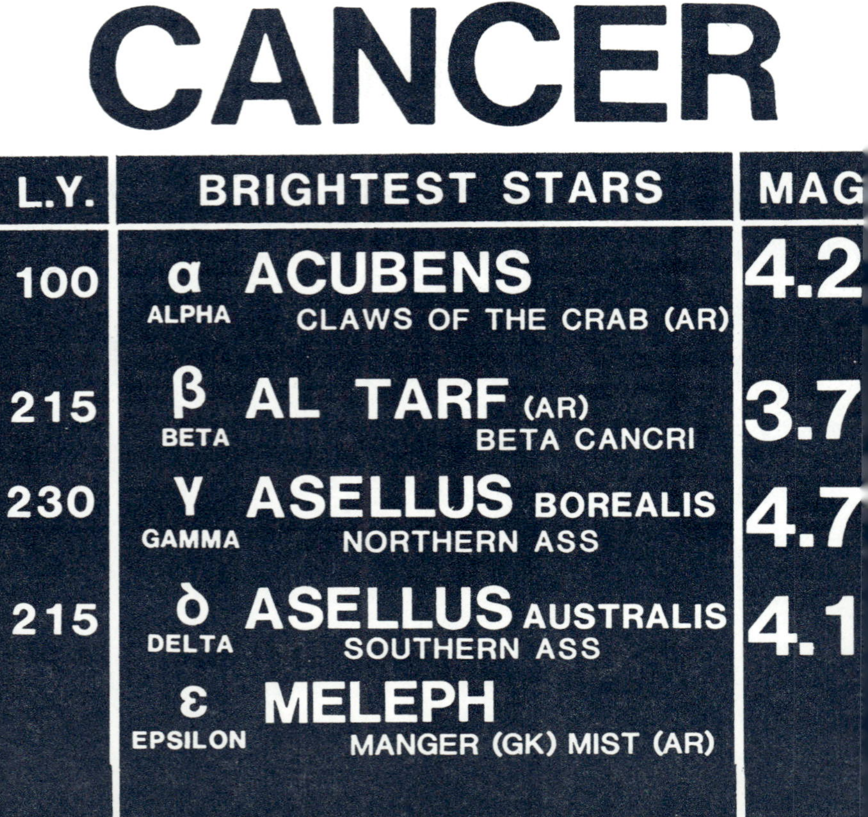

CANCER

L.Y.	BRIGHTEST STARS	MAG
100	α ALPHA ACUBENS CLAWS OF THE CRAB (AR)	4.2
215	β BETA AL TARF (AR) BETA CANCRI	3.7
230	γ GAMMA ASELLUS BOREALIS NORTHERN ASS	4.7
215	δ DELTA ASELLUS AUSTRALIS SOUTHERN ASS	4.1
	ε EPSILON MELEPH MANGER (GK) MIST (AR)	

visible to the right and slightly above the sought-after Cancer starfield. To the left, the bright star Regulus will become visible in the "sickle" of the constellation Leo (see "Project Leo," pages 51–53).

The reason we may see no stars in Cancer at first is that the brightest two, Al Tarf Beta (β) and Acubens Alpha (α) are only third and fourth magnitude. This makes them hard to spot where light pollution is a problem. But keep looking. Reconfirm both date and time and verify the correct 15–18-inch Starframe distance, even as your eyes get more and more adapted to the dark. Perhaps the central Asellus Australis, called the Southern Ass, the fourth-magnitude Delta (δ) star in Cancer, will gradually and faintly appear in sight just below the center of your Starframe. No white light, please—absolutely no white light: only the glow of your red flashlight as you confirm once more that you are really facing due south. Recheck your orientation with your compass. The size of your pictogram tracing should soon tell you whether you are viewing the right region.

It could, of course, be that there is an excessive amount of dust or moisture in the air and that seeing is less than good overall from your chosen location tonight. As you know from the weather, such conditions can change quickly and unexpectedly.

If you listen to your favorite music for an hour, even clouds may gradually dissolve and you may yet be able to discover the elusive Crab. Don't forget that during sixty minutes of waiting, your starfield will have moved to the right by one R.A. hour (i.e., by half a Starframe). You may want to wait until tomorrow night, or any of the many different date-time combinations that offer you enough "windows" to find Cancer on other dark (moonless) nights.

Once you have found, or think you have found, this least conspicuous pictogram in the entire Zodiac, a pair of binoculars can quickly confirm your search: Just to the right of the Delta (δ) star in Cancer mentioned above, you will discover for yourself a small swarming starcluster named the Beehive, or Praesepe. This conspicuous grouping, seen as a patch of mist by the unaided eye since ancient times, was given the number 44 by Charles Messier, thus its formal designation, M44. The cluster can be contained in the field-of-view of most binoculars. (See back cover.)

In his 1610 publication, *The Starry Messenger,* Galileo made a drawing of what, with his telescope, he resolved as forty stars in the Beehive. Today we know the irregular cluster consists of about three hundred fifty stars ranging in magnitude from six, the limit of what can be seen with the naked eye under dark skies, to faint stars at the telescopic limit. In the exact bottom right-hand corner of your Cancer Starframe shines the very bright first-magnitude star called Procyon. Together with a fainter second-magnitude star above and to its right, it constitutes the entire pictogram of Canis Minor, the Lesser Dog. This constellation consists of one tilted straight line just 5 degrees long. To learn about the nearby brightest star of all, Sirius, in Canis Major, the Greater Dog, see *Starwatch,* where the position of the dog star is shown and explained. Also see on page 132 this Starframe area superimposed on the Sky Calendar for June 1991, when Sirius will be visible in daytime during the total eclipse of the sun on July 11, 1991.

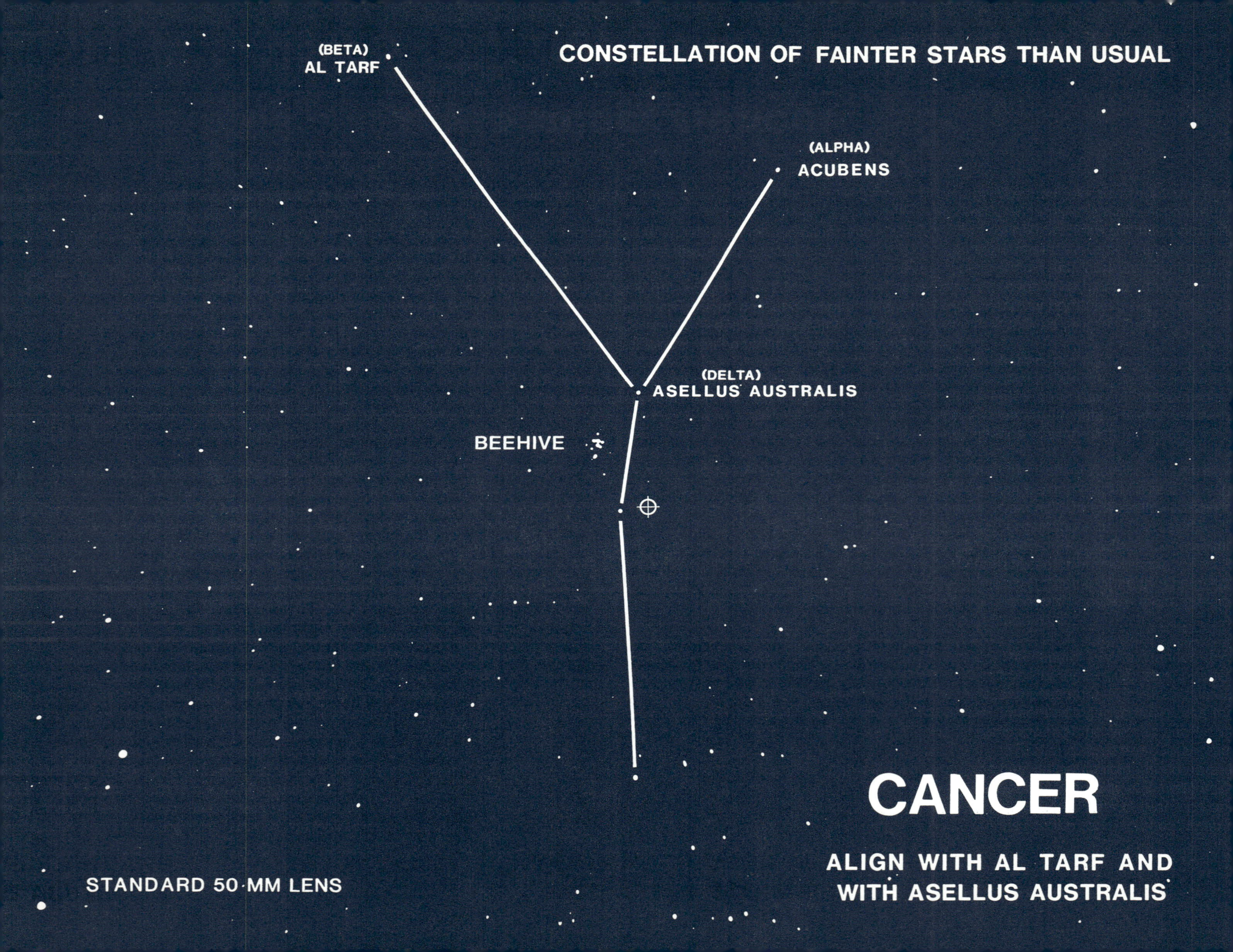
CONSTELLATION OF FAINTER STARS THAN USUAL
(BETA)
AL TARF
(ALPHA)
ACUBENS
(DELTA)
ASELLUS AUSTRALIS
BEEHIVE
CANCER
ALIGN WITH AL TARF AND
WITH ASELLUS AUSTRALIS
STANDARD 50 MM LENS

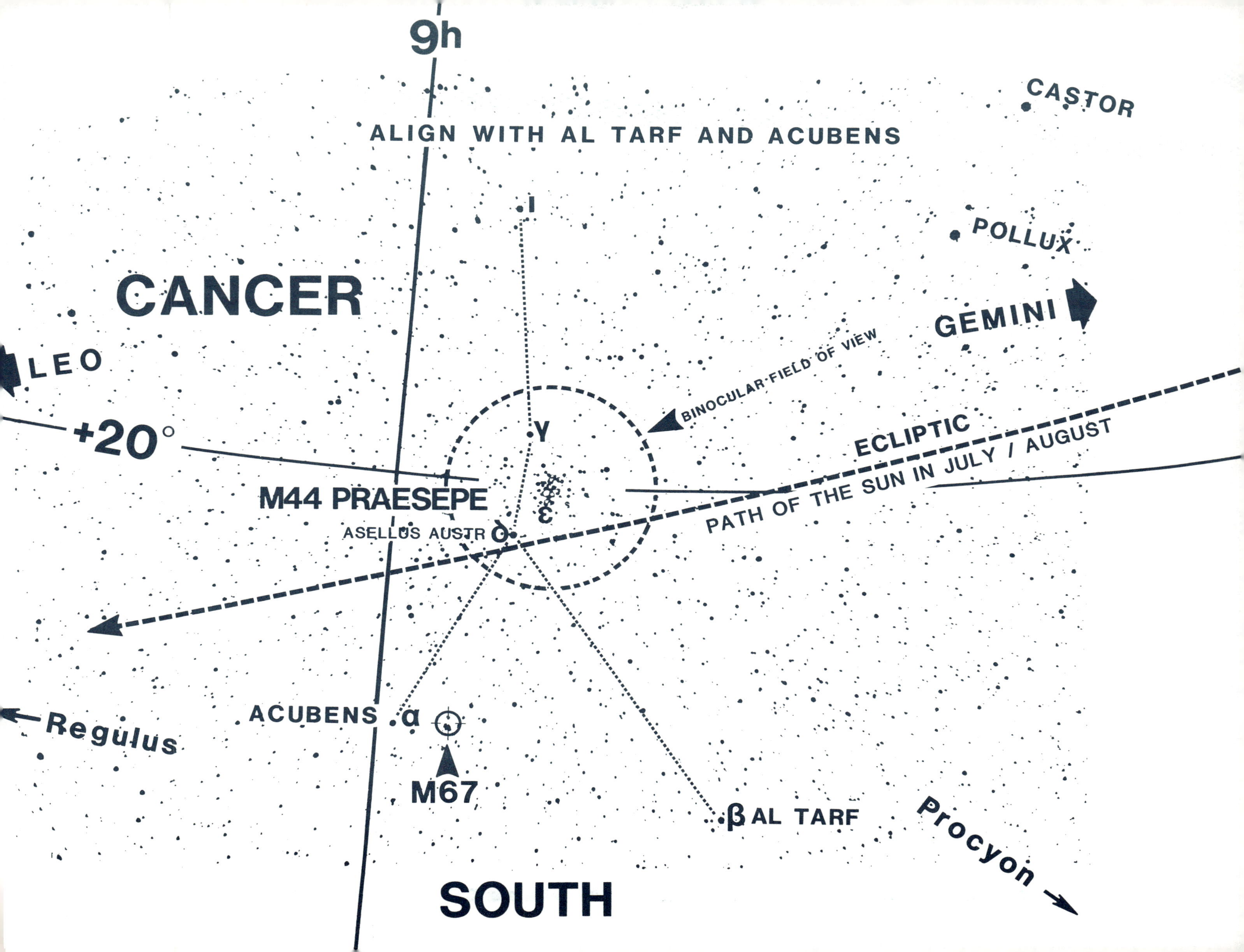
9h
CASTOR
ALIGN WITH AL TARF AND ACUBENS
POLLUX
CANCER
GEMINI
LEO
BINOCULAR FIELD OF VIEW
+20°
ECLIPTIC
PATH OF THE SUN IN JULY / AUGUST
M44 PRAESEPE
ASELLUS AUSTR δ
γ
ε
ι
ACUBENS α
Regulus
M67
β AL TARF
Procyon
SOUTH

Half Empty or Half Full?

When you can see the twin stars of Castor and Pollux in the sky but are unable to spot their fainter constellation companions, you may regard the heavens as philosophers have long viewed the proverbial half glass of water. It only depends on your attitude whether you think of the starry skies as half full or half empty. Here you even have an opportunity to tilt the balance in your favor.

The first alternative is selecting a dark observing site. If you are a city dweller you should travel south, to place your town and its shrouding light pollution behind you by half an hour, or even better, by a sixty-minute drive. You will notice significant improvements in seeing conditions.

A further option is night photography. I myself have an extraordinary and dark observing site one and a half hours outside of Los Angeles, but I often follow the rule of the bird in the hand being worth two in the bush. Once I found out that almost any camera can "see" more than even the miraculous human eye, my mind was made up. Today's "fast" (sensitive) film can *collect* faint starlight over precious time. Fifteen-to-thirty-second exposures can reveal what was formerly unseen or unseeable (see "Shooting Shooting Stars," pages 68–70). Such photography allows me to observe the stars year-round from my home, even under less than perfect conditions. That is how I photographed an entire series of important star records from my home. While I slept, my black-and-white film recorded thirteen sequential exposures of an exploding star (a *nova*). Call it serendipity: my good fortune lay in the fact that I did not yet know that such work was "impossible," that it simply could not be done from the center of a major city.

Under most conditions, the third method to help you get started is to concentrate your efforts on the bright moving planets that can be found only in the Zodiac and nowhere else. These heavenly wanderers match or exceed even Castor and Pollux in brightness, as mentioned on page 34. Just like the moon, the brightest planets can be observed and photographed even from downtown locations. You need only a basic publication like the inexpensive *Sky Calendar*[1] to acquaint you with where and when to find "evening" or "morning" planets and their positions in the Zodiac.

Generally, when planets are observed from week to week, they can be seen to move from west to east in relation to the fixed stars about them, as you stand facing south with your back to the north. This right-to-left movement of the planets is called *direct motion.* Sometimes, after gradually slowing down their travels in the Zodiac, planets change direction and journey from east to west. They apparently go in reverse *(retrograde)* motion.

Throughout history, this apparent motion of the planets puzzled both astrologers and astronomers, especially when the "normal" eastward planetary journeys were interrupted by periodic westward detours. To try to explain the seemingly erratic behavior of these bright objects in the sky, the most learned men in history invented ingenious explanations of "circles within circles" on which planets were said to travel. All of these early explanations were wrong, and none correctly solved the riddle of planetary motions. Astrologers and astronomers remained puzzled.

Any child who ever sat in a vehicle and watched another nearby conveyance move forward or backward has experienced the illusion of direct, as opposed to apparent, retrograde motion. The principles that apply are identical to those of the "carousel effect" (see "Seeing Is Not Believing," page 17). It may take a moment to grasp that some of the apparent motion of a nearby bus or train (in either direction) is caused by your own vehicle moving.

* * * * * * * *

[1] *Sky Calendar,* published by Abrams Planetarium, Michigan State University, East Lansing, Michigan 48824. They offer 365 invaluable *daily* guides, starting anytime. See a sample on page 131. It shows the June heavens for 1991.

WHY PLANETS SEEM TO MOVE BACK AND FORTH

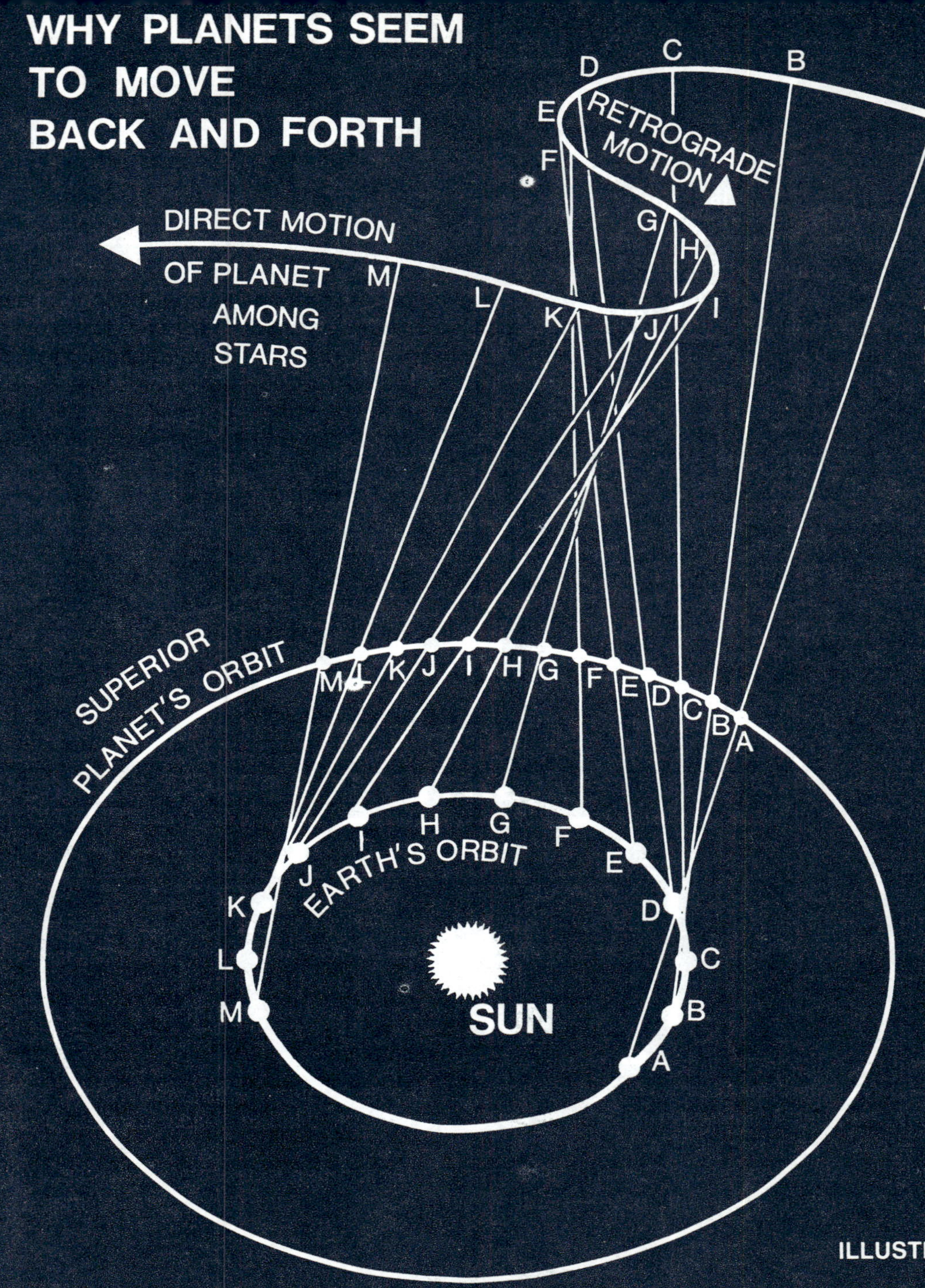

A careful look at illustration 08 will instantly unveil the seeming mystery of the ages and clearly show that planets always proceed in their east-west courses without interruption. It is just the view from our earth-in-motion perspective that creates the illusion of retrograde motion. The simple solution of such seemingly complex and puzzling problems lies at the heart of science. It is reminiscent of Copernicus's revolutionary theory, which placed the sun, rather than the earth, at the center of our universe.

We have long known that the planets circle in the heavens. In our overweening earth-centered *(geocentric)* conceit, we tried to invent workable solutions to justify direct and retrograde motions and make them conform to our preconceived idea that the earth lies unmoving at the center.

Not until Copernicus put our celestial house in order by suggesting a sun-centered *(heliocentric)* solar system could the skies be visualized as a vast circular track on which the planets travel at different speeds. It is little wonder that passengers aboard planet earth see neighboring planets apparently moving backward or forward as we are overtaking them—or are being overtaken, in turn.

When you combine planet observations from the worst light-polluted city skies with the possibilities offered by photography, you will soon discover that the skies may only *seem* devoid of stars. One night under sparkling skies in the mountains or desert, or a few hours by a deserted seashore or in a silent country meadow, can prove to you that light pollution is merely an *apparent* by-product of our technological age. The *real* skies await with serene blackness revealing myriad stars. Like countless diamonds in a black velvet-lined box, they fill the mysterious space beyond to overflowing.

ILLUSTRATION 08

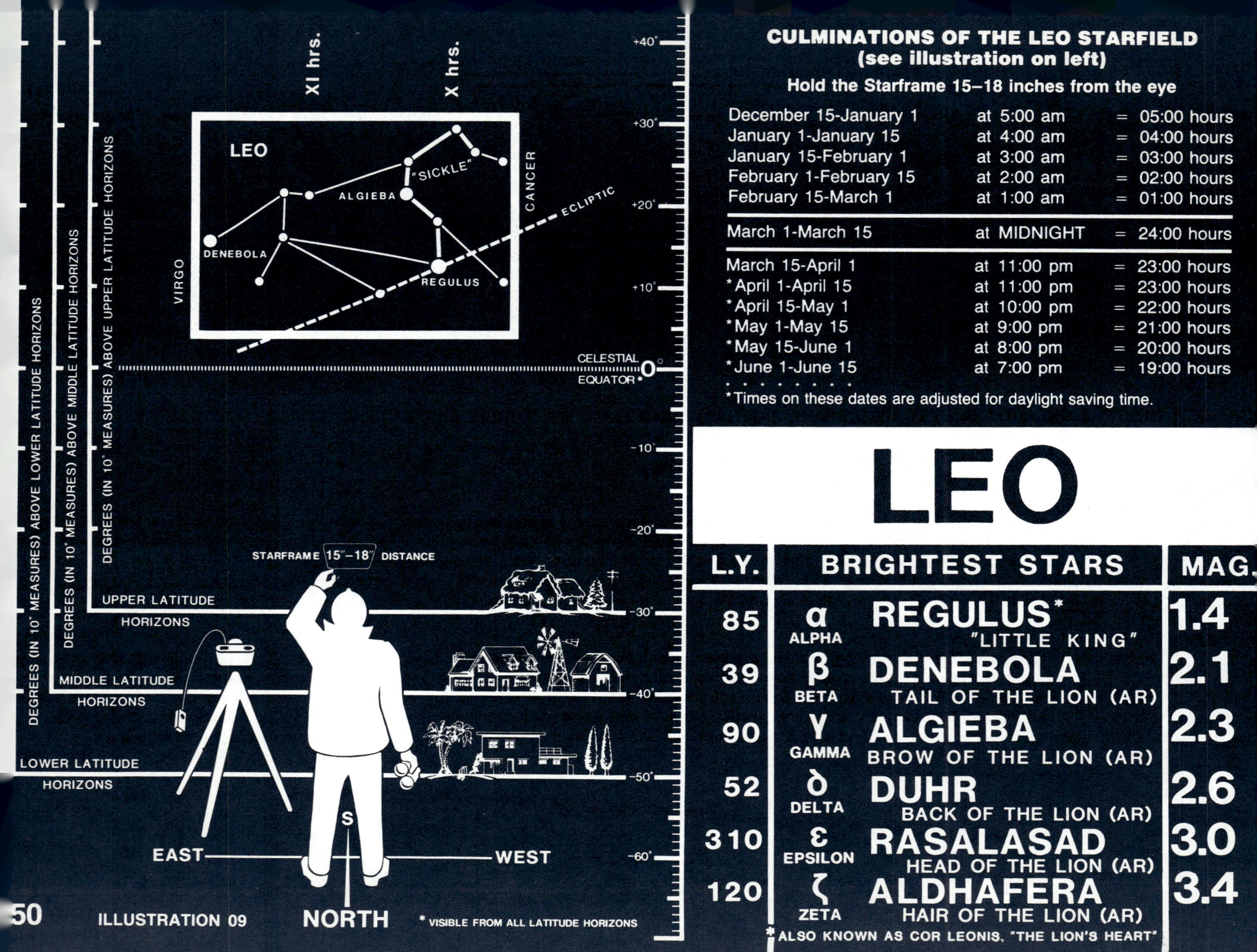

CULMINATIONS OF THE LEO STARFIELD
(see illustration on left)

Hold the Starframe 15–18 inches from the eye

December 15-January 1	at 5:00 am	= 05:00 hours
January 1-January 15	at 4:00 am	= 04:00 hours
January 15-February 1	at 3:00 am	= 03:00 hours
February 1-February 15	at 2:00 am	= 02:00 hours
February 15-March 1	at 1:00 am	= 01:00 hours
March 1-March 15	at MIDNIGHT	= 24:00 hours
March 15-April 1	at 11:00 pm	= 23:00 hours
*April 1-April 15	at 11:00 pm	= 23:00 hours
*April 15-May 1	at 10:00 pm	= 22:00 hours
*May 1-May 15	at 9:00 pm	= 21:00 hours
*May 15-June 1	at 8:00 pm	= 20:00 hours
*June 1-June 15	at 7:00 pm	= 19:00 hours

*Times on these dates are adjusted for daylight saving time.

LEO

L.Y.	BRIGHTEST STARS	MAG.
85	α ALPHA — REGULUS* "LITTLE KING"	1.4
39	β BETA — DENEBOLA — TAIL OF THE LION (AR)	2.1
90	γ GAMMA — ALGIEBA — BROW OF THE LION (AR)	2.3
52	δ DELTA — DUHR — BACK OF THE LION (AR)	2.6
310	ε EPSILON — RASALASAD — HEAD OF THE LION (AR)	3.0
120	ζ ZETA — ALDHAFERA — HAIR OF THE LION (AR)	3.4

*ALSO KNOWN AS COR LEONIS, "THE LION'S HEART"

Project Leo

You have a fine gathering of bright stars to help you find the constellation Leo quite easily. King among these is the first-magnitude Alpha (α) star in Leo called Regulus. Alpha (α) Leonis is one of the twenty-five brightest stars in the heavens. *Regulus* has long meant "little king." It was also known as Cor Leonis, "the heart of the lion." Between it and the second-magnitude Beta (β) star Denebola, descriptively called "the tail of the lion," Leo stretches across an entire Starframe, alerting you to the angular size of the king of beasts in the sky.

But it is another second-magnitude star, together with Alpha (α) Leonis, that will make Leo easy to spot even from brighter locations: the star Gamma (γ) Leonis, named Algieba ("the brow of the lion"), is part of a bright subgrouping known as "the sickle." This asterism has been recognized as the head and foreleg of Leo since earliest times. The form "Leonis" is the possessive form (also known as Genitive) of the name Leo. This form appears with each constellation.

Variable stars are an important part of the celestial scene and present a wonderful opportunity to perform serious scientific work with only a pair of binoculars (see "Binoculars," page 62). One such variable in Leo offers a fine chance to get a better understanding of what lies in store. The variable R in Leo, outlined in the negative Leo photo (page 53), shows you exactly where to look for it. Over a period of 312 days, it ranges from being visible to the naked eye at magnitude 4.4 to being invisible at magnitude 11 and back again. If you are interested in joining the eighty-year-old non-profit A.A.V.S.O. (American Association of Variable Star Observers), send a 9½-by-4½-inch, double-stamped, self-addressed envelope to the A.A.V.S.O., 25 Birch Street, Cambridge, Massachusetts 02138. In due course you will receive information on how you can participate in important astronomical science and space projects by watching, recording, and reporting the behavior of these sometimes explosive variables.

Several Messier objects are located in Leo. These include the faint and distant galaxies identified by the initial M of the famous Frenchman together with the number of the listing in his catalogue. M65, M66, M95, and M96 are such island universes twenty-five to thirty million light years distant, for which not only the darkest possible skies but also optical aids are required for observation. M65 and M66 are within binocular range.

To reconfirm the relationship between the apparent path of the sun and the Zodiac, please note that the star Regulus sits almost astride the ecliptic. In daytime and at night, it lies at the center of the zodiacal band, which in Leo is approximately 1½–2½ starframes above the southern horizon (see illustration 09).

AIM CAMERA AT THE HEART OF THE LION.

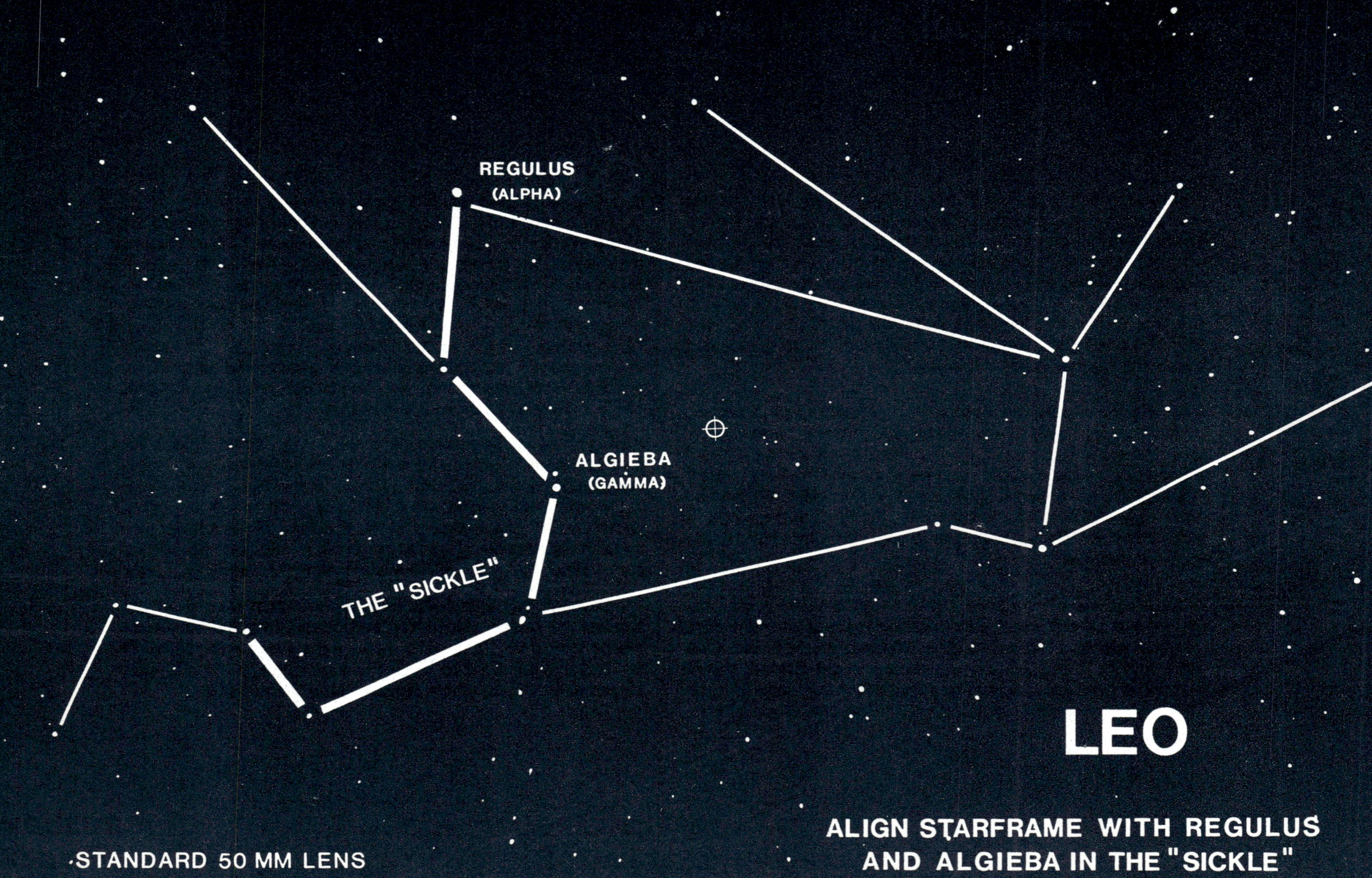

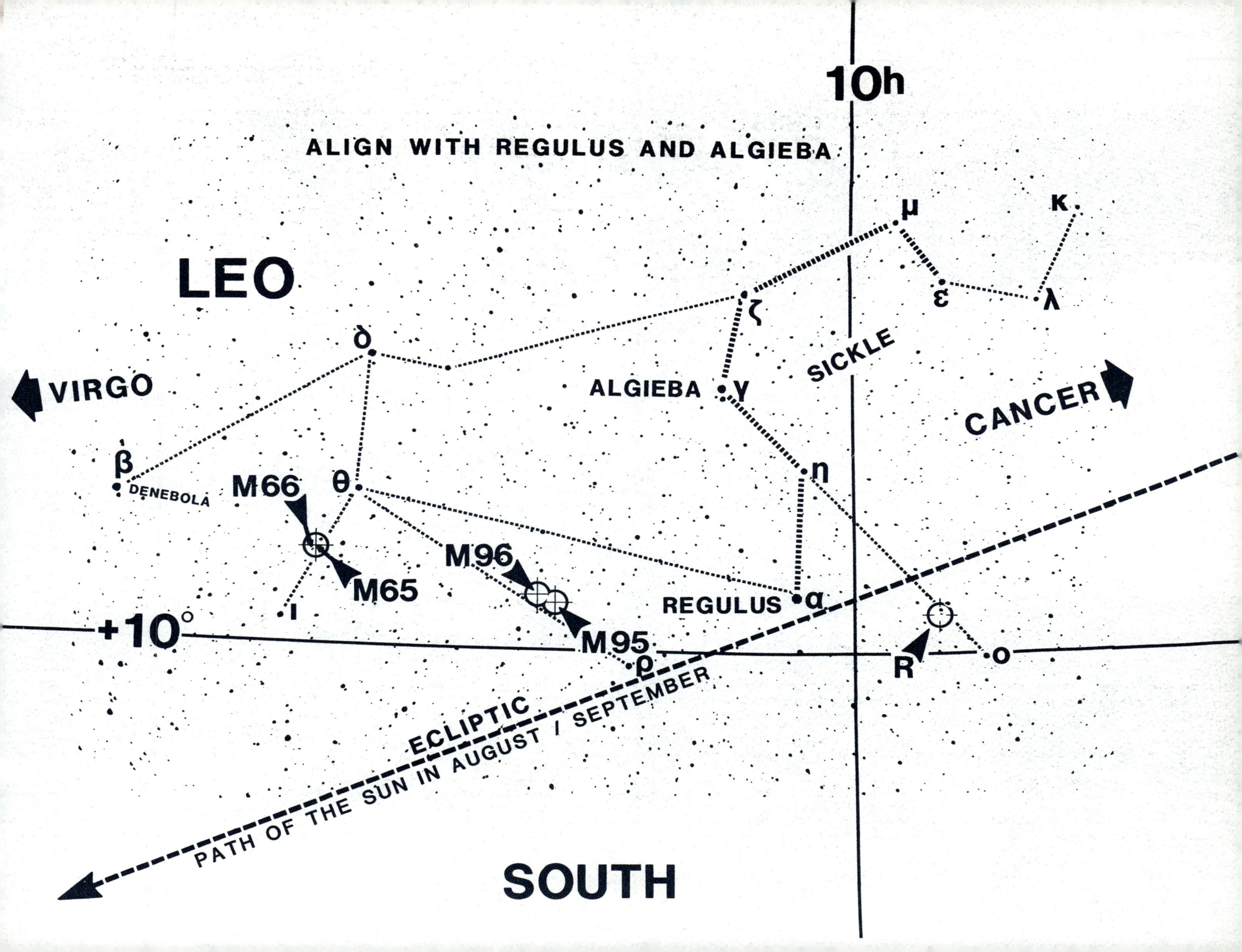
10h
ALIGN WITH REGULUS AND ALGIEBA
LEO
VIRGO
CANCER
SICKLE
ALGIEBA
REGULUS
DENEBOLA
M66
M65
M96
M95
R
+10°
ECLIPTIC
PATH OF THE SUN IN AUGUST / SEPTEMBER
SOUTH
μ
κ
ε
λ
ζ
δ
γ
η
β
θ
α
ι
ρ
o

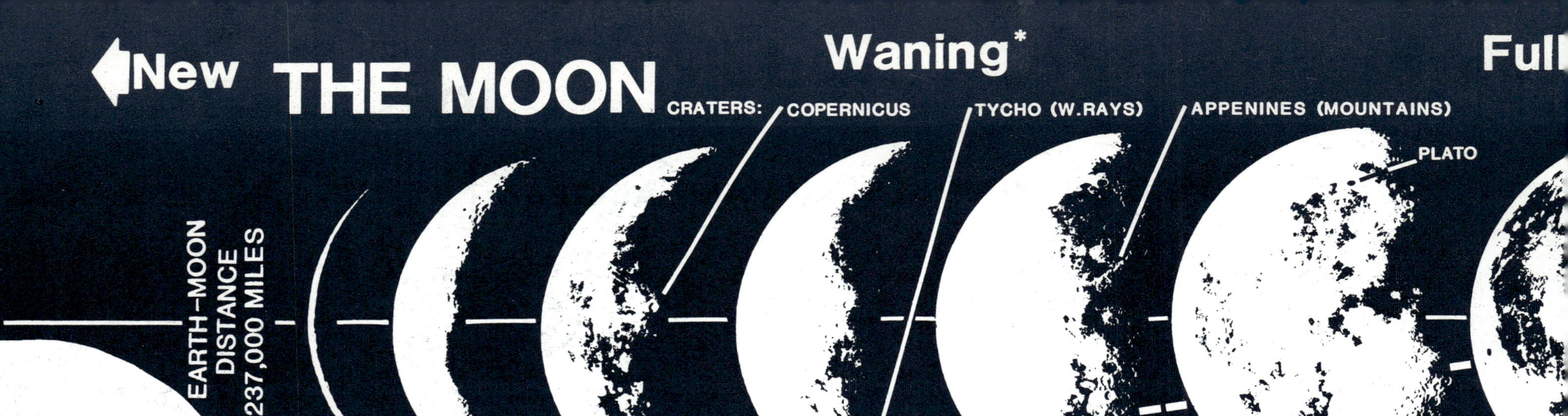

The Moon

There are two forms of "light intrusion" that are the bane of star-watchers. One is the often-mentioned light pollution, which cities, states, and even countries must address to reduce energy waste by the use of more efficient outdoor lighting systems. Through study of regional maps and actual exploration, it is generally possible to escape such local defilement by careful site selection to avoid the brightest locations.

The other light interference is global and perfectly natural. It has been with us since prehistoric times. By understanding the moon, we can anticipate and elude most lunar light. We can foretell the monthly cycles of the waxing, the full, and even the waning moon.

Moon **Waxing*** **New**

SEA OF SERENITY

SEA OF TRANQUILITY ⊕1969 LANDING

SEA OF CRISES

(DRY LUNAR FEATURES)

MOON DIAMETER 2,160 MILES

EXPOSURES: FROM 3 SECONDS (PARTIAL PHASES) TO 1/15 SECOND (FULL MOON). KEEP ACCURATE RECORDS.

ILLUSTRATION 10

Major observatories covetously reserve periods before moonrise or after moonset, when the skies are dark, for astronomical work only possible under the darkest skies. Merely the most worthy projects and their scientists may earn telescope time during new moon periods, when it is dark all night because then the moon is lost in the sun's daylight glare.

Astronomy books have helpful sections on lunar motions. There you may learn to understand what farmers have always known as a matter of course: the phases of the moon. Quite simply, moonlight is sunlight reflected back to earth from the moon, our nearest celestial neighbor. In keeping with the basic approach of this book, we will use the daily newspaper to explain how best to plan ahead, in order to see the sky under the darkest conditions.

As illustration 11 clearly shows, black skies prevail during the *last quarter* (last /4), while the moon is invisible *(new),* and during *first quarter* (first /4). In the almanac section of a good newspaper, the dates imprinted near the little diagrams tell the days when the moon may be seen in the exact phases pictured.

For brevity and simplicity, only the four principal stages are usually shown. The thirteen photographs in illustration 10 show other familiar intermediate appearances. To plan a productive observ-

ing program, it is useful to know moon phases in advance. The "zooming-abating" mnemonic jingle below, based on the directions of the script letters *a* and *z,* will help to show and tell at a glance where the moon is going.

Check your newspaper for all-dark new moon nights.

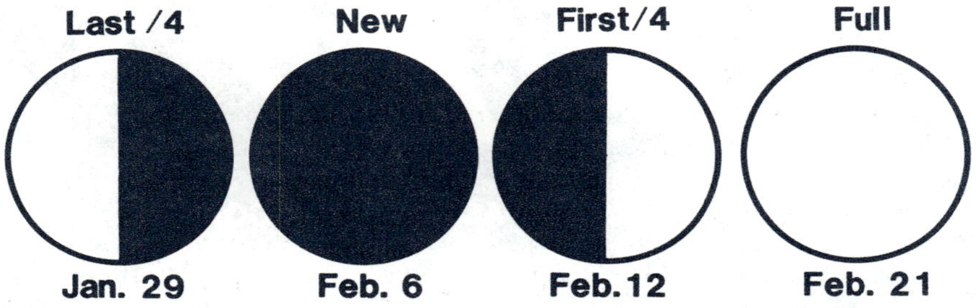

Last /4	New	First/4	Full
Jan. 29	Feb. 6	Feb. 12	Feb. 21

ILLUSTRATION 11

LUNAR A to Z

Z FOR ZOOMING TO FULL MOON

A FOR ABATING TO NEW,

TO TELL LUNAR WAXING OR WANING

ONE LOOK AT THE OUTLINE WILL DO.

As a rule, before and past *first quarter,* the moon rises progressively later in daytime, to set ever closer to midnight.

Around *full moon,* the lunar disc rises at sunset or first darkness, to set with approaching daylight.

Last quarter has the moon rising ever nearer—and even later than midnight. Moonrises past midnight allow increasingly long, dark evenings for star watching.

Near new moon, sun and lunar disc rise and set together. This offers the best and longest hours for observing and photographing, while the moon is actually "lost" in blinding sunlight during daytime hours.

The familiar phases of the moon as shown depend on its position in relation to the sun. To understand these phases, just think of exactly where the sun (the source of the reflected moonlight) is at any given time. Picture the moon being illuminated by the sun "from the right" at first quarter. Visualize the moon being blasted by the sun "face-on" at full moon, or spotlit "from the left" during last quarter (see illustration pages 54–55). Finally, imagine the lunar disc being lost to us in the glare of the distant daylight sun, which lies far beyond the nearby moon.

The moon is much smaller than the earth and close to us. The sun is very much larger but far, far away. This gives the appearance that they are the same size. Nothing could be further from the truth.

The moon has a north and a south pole. The photographs shown here have "north up." This is how we see the moon in the sky or through binoculars. For telescopes, which reverse images, you will have to turn the book upside down to identify the various landmarks.

The orbit of the moon around the earth and the path of the earth about the sun form planes that are slightly inclined towards each other. This inclination of 5 degrees means that the moon may travel anywhere from 5 degrees above to 5 degrees below the ecliptic. This places it well within the band of the Zodiac, our primary area of interest and observation.

Project Virgo

"Are you an amateur astronomer?" I asked the beautiful woman I had noticed much earlier, while it was still light.

"Oh, no," she replied.

"Then what brings you to the Riverside Telescope Makers' Conference?"[1] I continued.

"My boyfriend. He builds telescopes. I like to come up here and spend a few nights under the stars in a sleeping bag."

"What's your sign?" I inquired.

"I'm a Virgo," she breathed, with an inflection in her voice that hardly suggested the Italian *Vergine*'s allegorical representation of innocence and virtue. "I was born on September sixth."

"Would you like to see the brightest star in the constellation Virgo?" I suggested.

"Oh, I'd just love to," she cooed. "Can one see it tonight?"

"There it is." I stood close to her, and with the silhouette of my hand pointed at the bright Alpha (α) star in Virgo. "This is Spica, which means 'ear of wheat.' It is the brightest star in the constellation you claim for your own. An ear of corn is what the heavenly Virgin is said to hold in her left hand." From there it took only a little time to tell and weave the lore of the palm branch in the virgin's right hand.

I had a Virgo Stellaphane Starframe with glowing stardots to help

* * * * * * * * *

[1] Riverside Telescope Makers' Conference, held annually on Memorial Day weekend in the San Bernardino Mountains of Southern California.

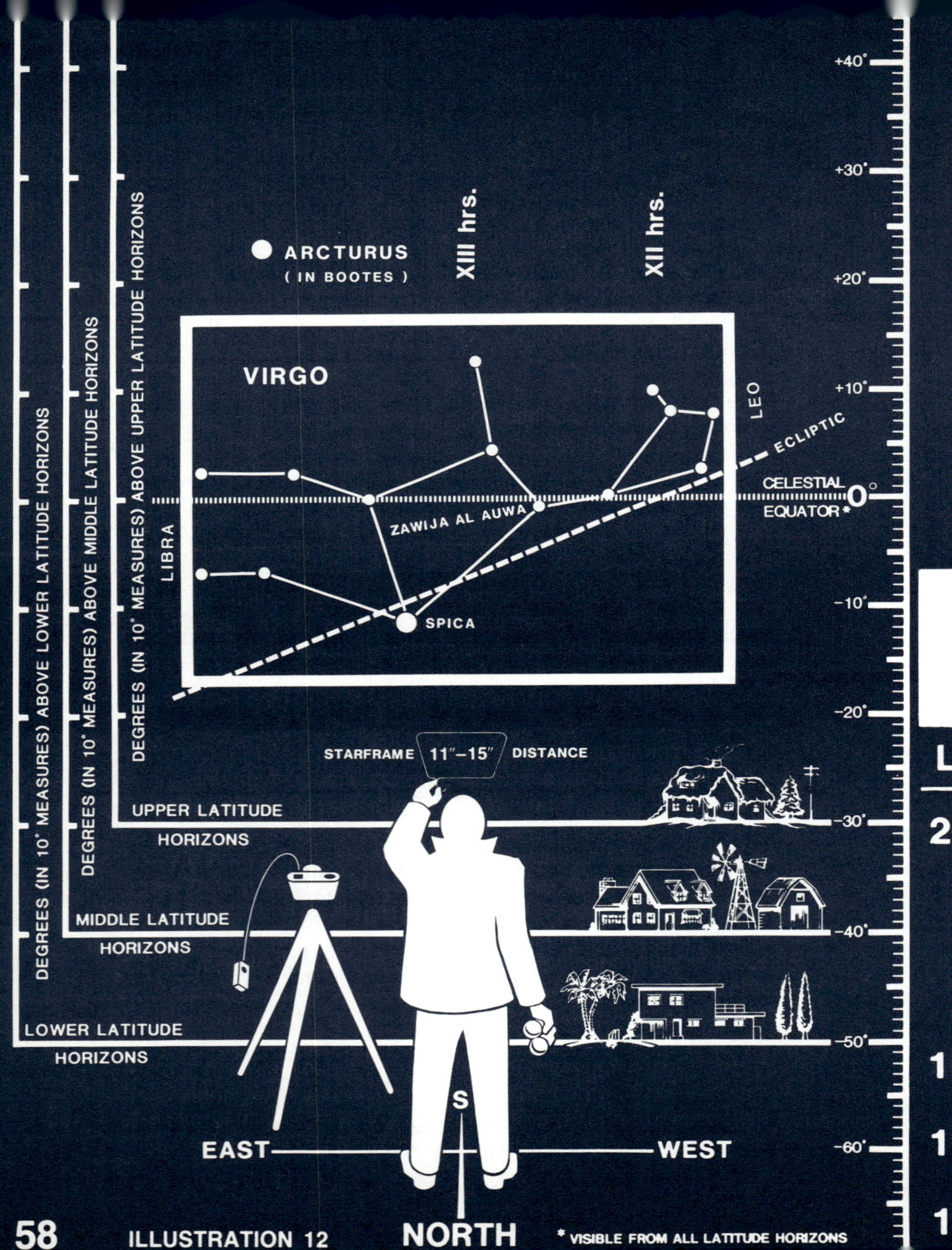

ILLUSTRATION 12

*VISIBLE FROM ALL LATITUDE HORIZONS

CULMINATIONS OF THE VIRGO STARFIELD (see illustration on left)

Hold the Starframe only 11–15 inches from the eye

February 1-February 15	at 5:00 am	= 05:00 hours
February 15-March 1	at 4:00 am	= 04:00 hours
March 1-March 15	at 3:00 am	= 03:00 hours
*March 15-April 1	at 2:00 am	= 02:00 hours
*April 1-April 15	at 2:00 am	= 02:00 hours
*April 15-May 1	at 1:00 am	= 01:00 hours
*May 1-May 15	at MIDNIGHT	= 24:00 hours
*May 15-June 1	at 11:00 pm	= 23:00 hours
*June 1-June 15	at 10:00 pm	= 22:00 hours
*June 15-July 1	at 9:00 pm	= 21:00 hours
*July 1-July 15	at 8:00 pm	= 20:00 hours
*July 15-August 1	at 7:00 pm	= 19:00 hours

*Times on these dates are adjusted for daylight saving time.

VIRGO

L.Y.	BRIGHTEST STARS	MAG.
260	α ALPHA **SPICA** EAR OF WHEAT (LATIN)	0.9
32	β BETA **ZAVIJAVA** THE ANGLE (AR)	3.8
36	γ GAMMA **ZAWIJA AL AUWA** THE CORNER IN THE ANGLE (AR)	2.7
150	δ DELTA **DELTA VIRGINIS**	3.3
100	ε EPSILON **ALMUREDIN** WINE GATHERER (AR) ALSO KNOWN AS **VINDEMIATRIX**	2.8
140	η **ZANIAH** ANGLE STAR (AR)	4.0

her find the rest of the constellation. It was easy in the mountain darkness, under perfectly black starlit skies at a seven-thousand-foot altitude. Carefully I brought my Starframe hand close to her face so that she would see the entire wide-ranging pictogram.

Virgo is so spread out in right ascension that you too must hold your Stellaphane Starframe only 11–15 inches from your eye. This can be compared to employing a wide-angle lens with a shorter focal length of 35 millimeters, as against the standard 50- or 55mm length. That is exactly how I photographed the Virgo starfield to get all of it into the picture. (See back cover.)

In Virgo you have only one anchor star, merely one single beacon of first magnitude by which to navigate through the celestial expanse of the constellation. Spica can be seen even under poor conditions. By holding the Starframe at the shorter framing distance of 11–15 inches, you expand your field of view tremendously. Therefore, chances are greater that you will see at least one planet (or possibly more) within or near your Starframe, which can confuse even old starhands.

Aiming binoculars on any of these bright interlopers, can always help to reveal *Jupiter* through its tiny Jovian moons. These extend neatly on one or both sides of this dazzler. Even *Saturn,* the ringed planet, will show its elongated form and thus give itself away. This leaves only *Mars* in serious contention as a possible competitor for your attention. But Mars's reddish color would distinguish it from the brilliant white of Spica. *Venus* only culminates during daylight hours and therefore cannot be seen except in the early evening or before dawn. Mercury, too close the sun, would only appear in our starfields near sunrise or sunset when the constellations must, of course, be close to the horizon and far from culmination. Finally, the light of planets is usually quite still while stars often twinkle.

Another important difference between wandering planets and the fixed star Spica is motion. This normally can be observed over a period of one week, and you may want to mark your Starframe with an adhesive arrow or dot to help you reveal any direct or retrograde movement of planets (see page 49). Photographic records that you take will soon separate wandering planets from the stationary stars anywhere in the celestial carousel.

The Virgo pictogram culminates 45 degrees above the southern horizon, which equals one and a half or two Starframes in elevation, as pictured on page 58. Spica will be the southernmost star in the starfield, closest to the bottom of the Starframe, and easily the brightest object unless planets are present.

After you have found Spica and "covered" it with your Starframe dot, be on the lookout for Zawija al Auwa, the Gamma (γ) star, which at third magnitude is much fainter than Spica. But be patient. Once your eyes have become properly accustomed to the dark, this star may gradually emerge and glow, eventually to reveal the other, fainter companion stars. Its name in Arabic means "corner of the angle."

Do not forget that you need a shorter (11–15-inch) string gauge to encompass the wide angular area of Virgo. With Alpha (α) and Gamma (γ) in Virgo, you can position your Starframe correctly.

It is nearby, between the Beta (β) and the Gamma (γ) stars, that the sun crosses the equator in the sky. It marks the date and the place of the autumn equinox (see pages 31–32). With binoculars, be on the lookout for the variable stars R, S, U, and RS. You may also want to try to spot some of the Messier galaxies in the region (see page 51). The Virgo "milky ways" are 50–70 million light years away from earth. Each contains hundreds of millions or billions of stars. Just glimpsing one of these faint wisps will set you to wondering whether we are alone in the universe, or if somewhere in space there is extraterrestrial intelligence.

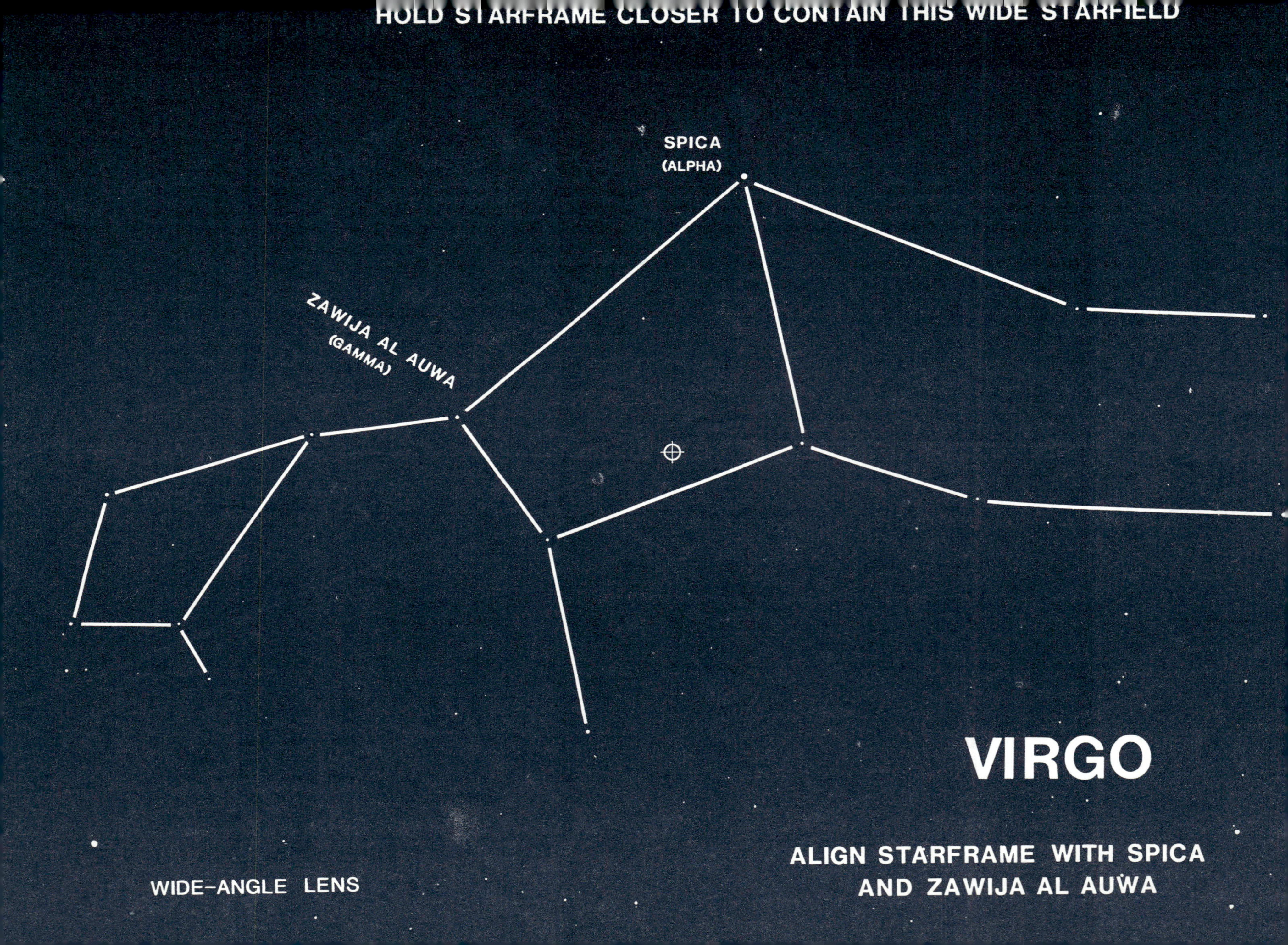

HOLD STARFRAME CLOSER TO CONTAIN THIS WIDE STARFIELD

SPICA
(ALPHA)

ZAWIJA AL AUWA
(GAMMA)

VIRGO

ALIGN STARFRAME WITH SPICA
AND ZAWIJA AL AUWA

WIDE-ANGLE LENS

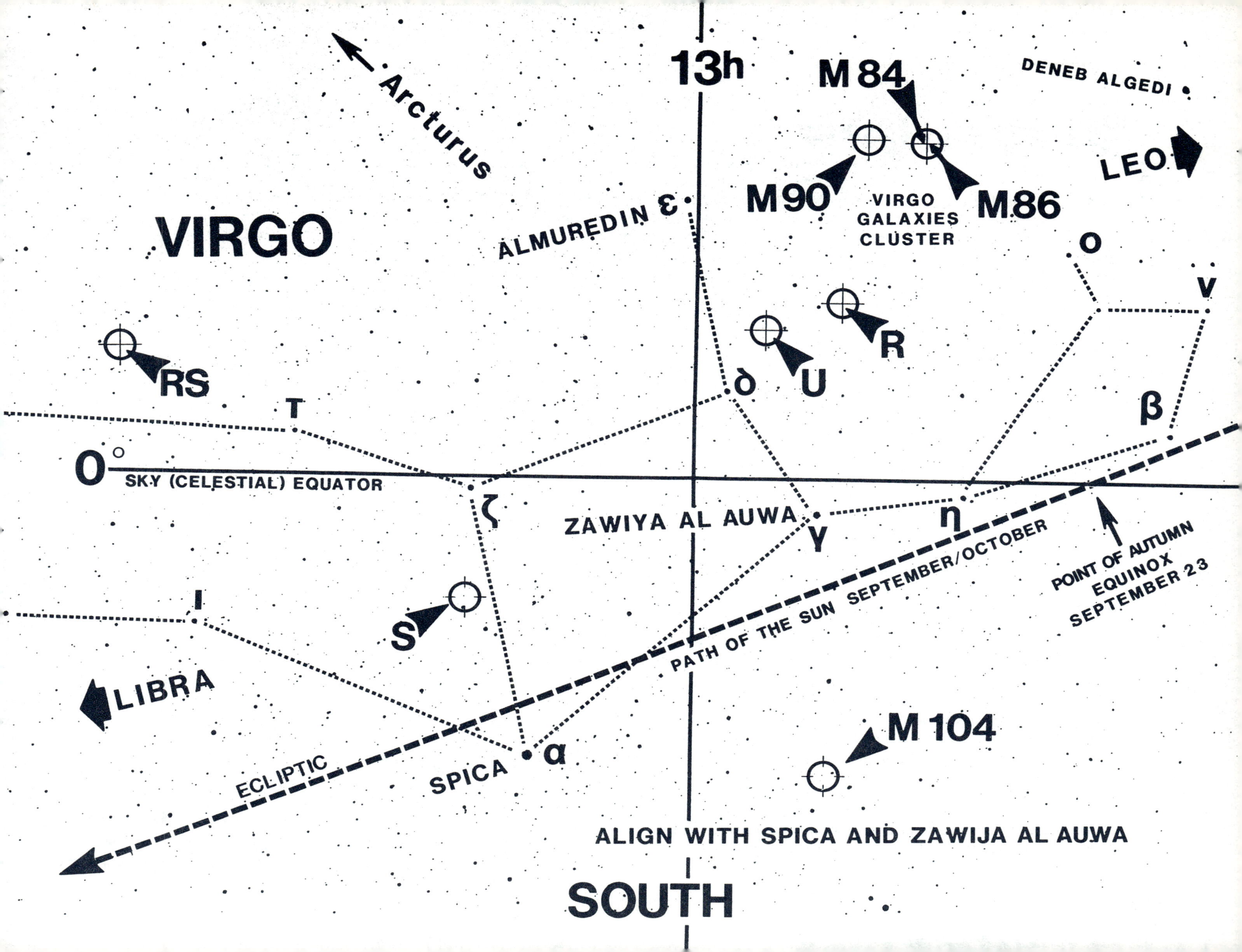
13h
Arcturus
M 84
DENEB ALGEDI
LEO
M90
M86
VIRGO GALAXIES CLUSTER
ALMUREDIN ε
VIRGO
o
v
R
U
RS
δ
T
β
O
SKY (CELESTIAL) EQUATOR
ζ
ZAWIYA AL AUWA
γ
η
PATH OF THE SUN SEPTEMBER/OCTOBER
POINT OF AUTUMN EQUINOX SEPTEMBER 23
S
LIBRA
M 104
ECLIPTIC
SPICA
α
ALIGN WITH SPICA AND ZAWIJA AL AUWA
SOUTH

Binoculars

Next to the unaided eye, the most popular optical aid to visual astronomical observation is a pair of binoculars. In value per dollar spent, they far exceed any telescope. Binoculars are compact because they employ *folded optics,* using prisms in combination with lenses. The lenses nearest the eye are called the *oculars,* or *eyepieces,* while the larger glasses, which may be pointed at the sky, are called the *objective lenses.* Binoculars are rated according to their magnifications and the diameters of their objective lenses. A 7 × 50 pair is perfect for starwatching. It provides magnification of 7 times with both objective lenses 50 millimeters (2 inches) in diameter. This aperture offers good light grasp. A rating of 7 × 35 is standard, and 10 × 50 offers more magnification.

On two of our Stellaphane starmaps, binocular fields of view are circled. The areas outlined are circles a little larger than the round hook portion of a coathanger Starframe when held 15–18 inches from the eye. You can compare magnifications in relation to the normally visible field of view during any day. At night, try the monthly starfield. The Beehive in Cancer (page 47) and the Pleiades in Taurus (page 123) are good testing regions.

A fine pair of binoculars will give you more optical reach than was available to famous astrological or astronomical scholars from the beginning of time up to the age of Galileo, in the sixteenth century, when the first telescopes were invented. As can be verified while viewing the moon (see pages 54–55,), all fields are seen "the right way up." This presents a notable advantage over telescopes, which turn targets upside down, substituting south for north. Binoculars show us exactly what the eye(s) see, while bringing things considerably closer.

Try viewing any distant field of view with one unaided eye while looking through half a binocular (a monocular) with the other. This allows you to estimate binocular magnification quickly. Establish how many diameters fit into the 30 degrees of your Starframe (about four such circles will tell you the angular field of view of your instrument: 30 degrees divided by 4 = 7½ degrees).

Never ever aim binoculars or other optical aids at the sun—not even near it. This could result in permanent blindness, because the glaring light of the sun would become even further intensified through magnification via any lens diameters. Irreversible eye damage is possible in the flash of a moment.

Try to become familiar with a binocular instrument, which acts like two telescopes mounted side by side. It permits convenient, near-normal, in-depth vision. Learn to look through binoculars quickly by literally flipping them in position while still looking at targets with the naked eye. You will soon appreciate the ease with which they can be used, especially because of their accustomed fields of view. Unlike telescopes, these bear a practical relationship to what our eyes are accustomed to seeing.

Binoculars literally focus your eyes—and all your attention—on specific areas in the sky. This may help you feel that you are actually entering the realm of the stars. Relax and make yourself comfortable as you scan the heavens through the porthole of your own spacecraft.

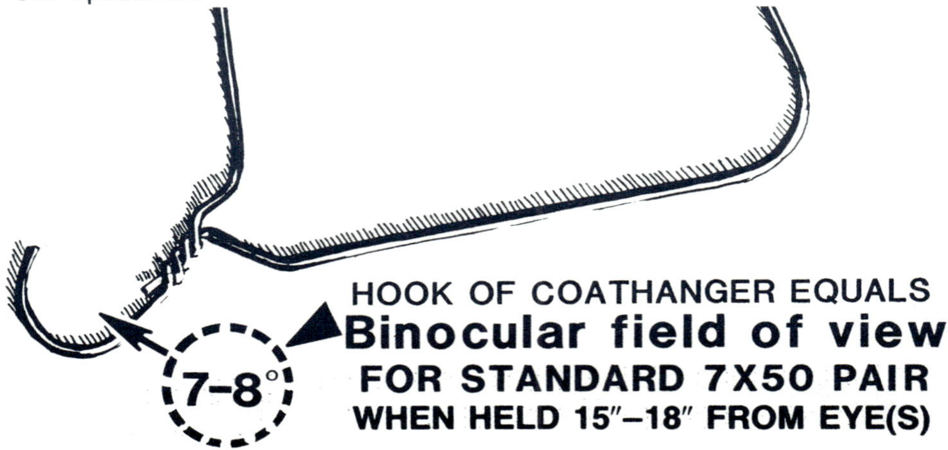

Project Libra

Even the Greeks did not regard the stars in Libra as a balance, although the libra was a Roman measure of weight used in scales. In classical Rome, the starfield Libra was, in fact, part of the more ancient and adjoining constellation of the Scorpion. The Arabic names of the brightest stars in Libra support the claim that the constellation was added as the twelfth sign of the Zodiac by Julius Caesar.

The Alpha (α) Libra star is still called by its Arabic name, Zuben Elgenubi, "the right claw of the Scorpion," or the southern claw. The Beta (β) Libra star bears the name of Zuben Elschamali, "the left claw of the Scorpion," or the northern claw. Both these names relate to Arabia. These brightest Libra stars, at magnitudes 2.7 and 2.6, should pose little problem for observation.

Hold the Stellaphane Starframe at the regular 15–18-inch distance above the compass point due south, at the angle as shown. This is an easy elevation for a tripod-mounted camera to imitate. The compact constellation of Libra in its entirety will now be contained in your Starframe (see illustration 13).

The only stars that may mislead you here are the bright stars of the neighboring starfield of Scorpius. These are grouped together in the lower left of your Starframe. The brightest of these is the Scorpion star Antares (see "Project Scorpius," pages 71–75). At first you may assume that this bright object is a planet. The very name Antares actually means "rival of Mars," because with its reddish color the bright star was often mistaken for the equally bright and reddish martian planet. Don't forget to check the region for the planet Mars or others that may be wandering through the starfield (see page 59 for a binocular check method), or the planet position charts through the years 2000 on pages 133–134.

You might as well use the first-magnitude Scorpion star Antares to help you align your Libra constellation Starframe. Place this first-magnitude (0.9-) star in the bottom left-hand corner of your Starframe. At the correct distance of 15–18 inches, both Alpha (α) in

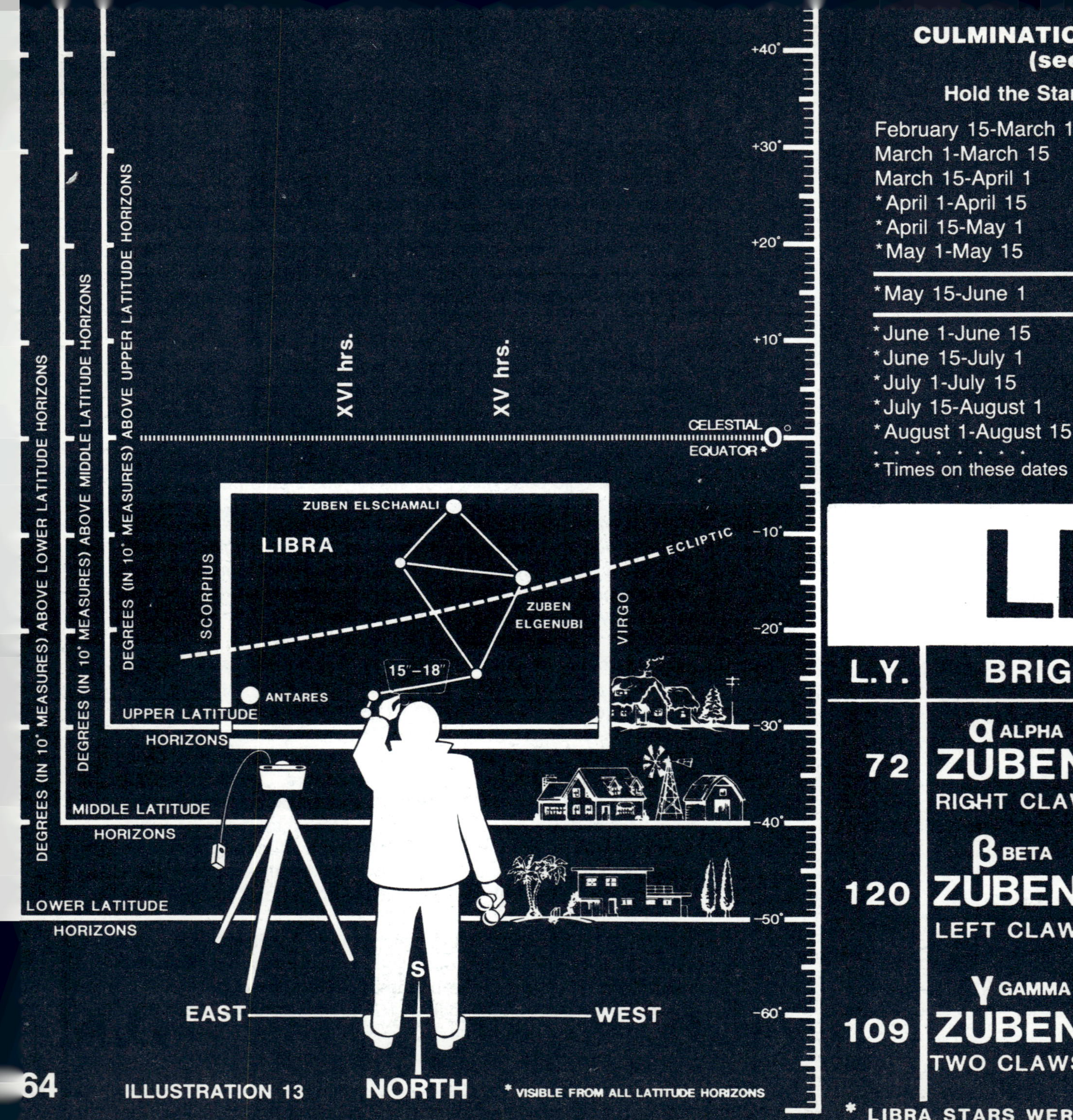

ILLUSTRATION 13

CULMINATION OF THE LIBRA STARFIELD (see illustration on left)

Hold the Starframe 15–18 inches from the eye

February 15-March 1	at 5:00 am	=	05:00 hours
March 1-March 15	at 4:00 am	=	04:00 hours
March 15-April 1	at 3:00 am	=	03:00 hours
*April 1-April 15	at 3:00 am	=	03:00 hours
*April 15-May 1	at 2:00 am	=	02:00 hours
*May 1-May 15	at 1:00 am	=	01:00 hours
*May 15-June 1	at MIDNIGHT	=	24:00 hours
*June 1-June 15	at 11:00 pm	=	23:00 hours
*June 15-July 1	at 10:00 pm	=	22:00 hours
*July 1-July 15	at 9:00 pm	=	21:00 hours
*July 15-August 1	at 8:00 pm	=	20:00 hours
*August 1-August 15	at 7:00 pm	=	19:00 hours

*Times on these dates are adjusted for daylight saving time.

LIBRA

L.Y.	BRIGHTEST STARS	MAG.
72	α ALPHA ZUBEN ELGENUBI RIGHT CLAW OF THE SCORPION (AR) THE SOUTHERN CLAW	2.7
120	β BETA ZUBEN ELSCHAMALI LEFT CLAW OF THE SCORPION (AR) THE NORTHERN CLAW	2.6
109	γ GAMMA ZUBEN HAKRABI * TWO CLAWS OF THE SCORPION (AR)	4.0

* LIBRA STARS WERE ONCE PART OF SCORPIUS

Libra at magnitude 2.7 and Beta (β) Librae at brightness 2.6 should easily reveal themselves about one R.A. hour to the right (west) and 15 degrees above (north of) Antares.

It is important to point out that since we observed the constellation of Virgo, we have just—like the sun—crossed south of the celestial equator. Libra can be called a southern celestial hemisphere constellation. It is visible to northern observers even though it lies in the sky between −10 degrees and −30 degrees, ranging from 14 hours to 16 hours in right ascension (R.A.) (see illustration 14).

When astronomers try to find exact positions in the sky, they use a system of *coordinates.* These are created at the intersections where horizontal circles measured in hours of right ascension (R.A.) and vertical degrees of *declination (Dec.)* cross. The celestial coordinates for the star Alpha (α) Librae are R.A. $14^{h}48^{m}$, Dec. −16 degrees 02′. The official boundaries are outlined in the illustration where the constellation borders are clearly shown. The principal starfield pictogram is much smaller. See below.

ILLUSTRATION 14

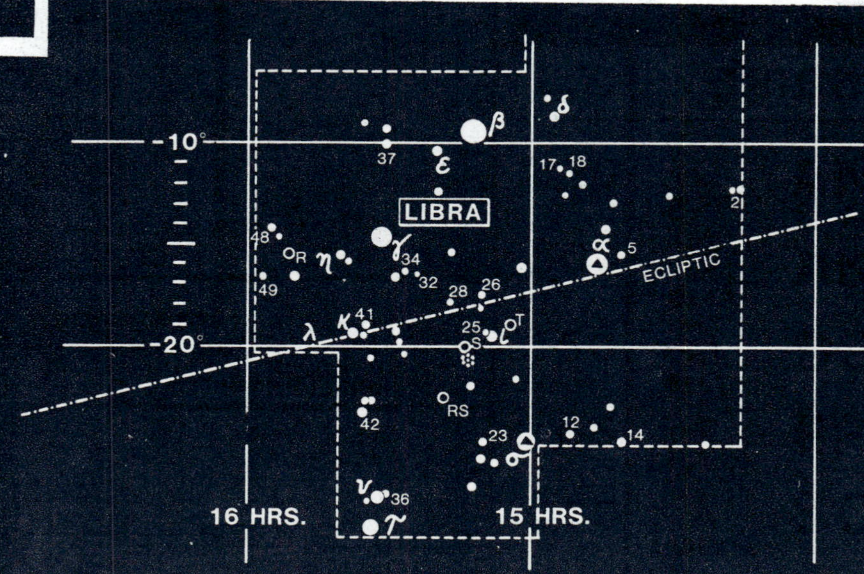

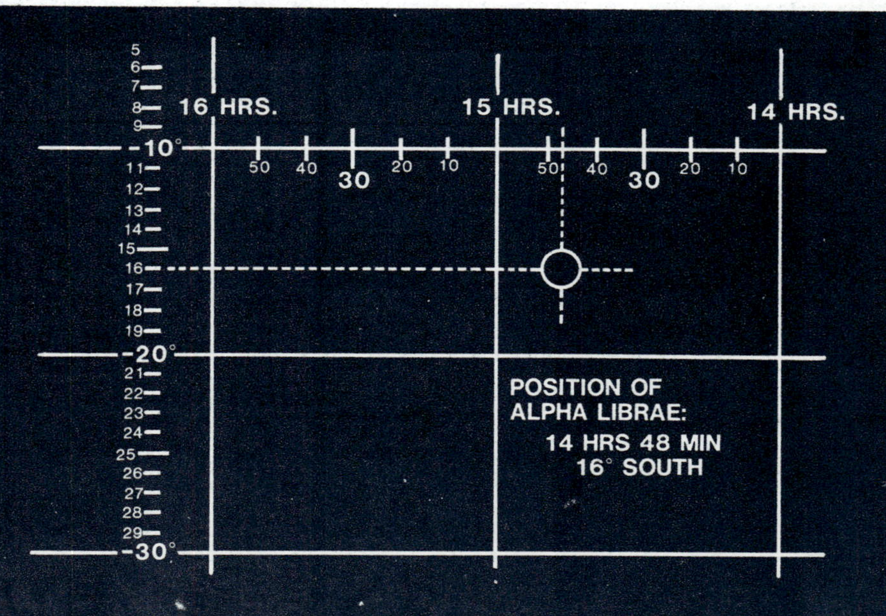

(ALPHA SCORPII)
ANTARES

LIBRA

(ALPHA)
ZUBEN ELGENUBI

(BETA)
ZUBEN ELSCHAMALI

STANDARD 50 MM LENS

ALIGN WITH ZUBEN ELGENUBI
AND ZUBEN ELSCHAMALI

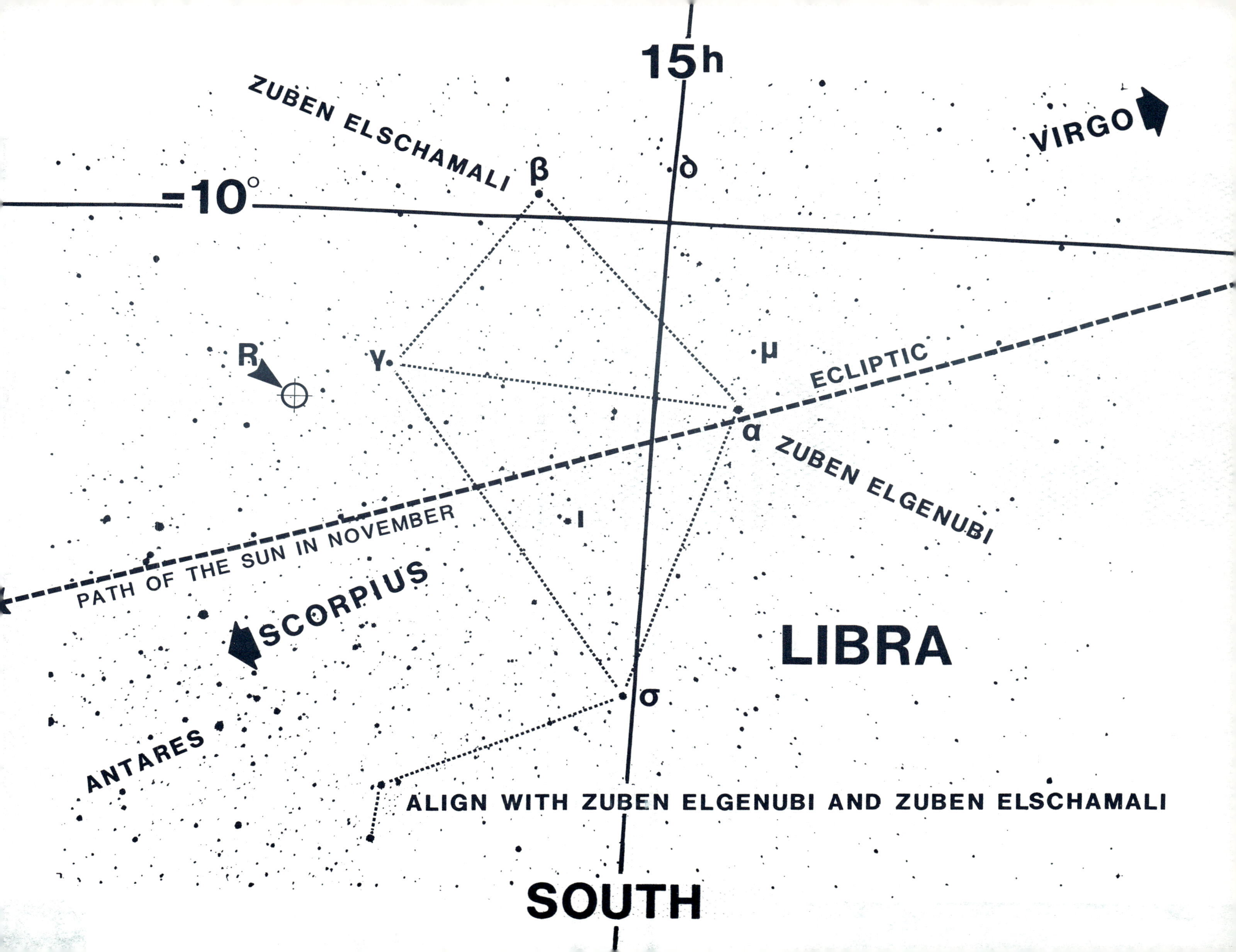

15h

ZUBEN ELSCHAMALI

VIRGO

β

δ

−10°

R

γ

μ

ECLIPTIC

α

ZUBEN ELGENUBI

ι

PATH OF THE SUN IN NOVEMBER

SCORPIUS

LIBRA

σ

ANTARES

ALIGN WITH ZUBEN ELGENUBI AND ZUBEN ELSCHAMALI

SOUTH

Shooting Shooting Stars

To photograph shooting stars (meteors) in the sky, all one needs to do is load a camera with fast (sensitive) film and put it on a steady tripod aimed at the sky with a wide-open fast (low f/number such as f 1.4) lens focused on infinity (∞). To familiarize yourself with *time exposures,* open the shutter for 15–30 seconds, then increasing the exposure time to 1 minute, redoubling to 2, 4, or even 8 minutes. That's all. Repeat this series four times for a roll of twenty-four pictures. Of course, the longer you leave your shutter open, the better your chance of catching a meteor on your film.

Today's cameras can do everything for you, which is why an older single-lens reflex (SLR) model bought in a pawnshop may do just as well as a new one. All it needs is a fast standard lens. A 50mm f/1.4 or f/1.8 lens will do for any sky photography. If you visit a good camera shop, the sales staff can best help if you tell them that you want to shoot stars in the nightsky. You will learn that speed is the name of the game. Don't let anyone try to sell you a slow "tele-lens" or a zoom lens. You want to buy speed, because you already know that the celestial carousel is in motion and that time is of the essence to arrest the stars in the sky.

Buy the fastest 50mm standard lens you can afford. An f/1.4 lens costs more than an f/1.8 or an f/2. The fastest lens can collect the most starlight in the shortest time. The equivalent of a 5-second exposure through an f/1.4 lens takes 8¼ seconds through an f/1.8. It takes 10 seconds with an f/2. You will need twice as long again with an f/2.8 lens.

In the popular 35mm film format, Kodak, Fuji, and others are ever racing for supremacy in maximum film speed. Don't forget, it is the newest films that can make even older cameras into sensitive new starlight collectors. Even the fast new Polaroid 612 film can be used for instant results to shoot constellations.

1

2

3

4

5

ILLUSTRATION 15

Keep a Detailed Log

Before we go any further, the importance of your astronomical notebook must be reemphasized. By writing down exactly what, where, when, and how you were doing, you will be creating an invaluable source of experience for yourself. For instance, this will allow you to copy all such information on the backs of your photographs when the film is returned by the lab. If you shoot with slide film, which is preferable, you can transfer all your notes onto the cardboard frames in which mounted slides are returned. Then you can instantly see the difference in results between a 15-second, a 30-second, and a 4-minute exposure. There is a big difference, as you can quickly find out (see "Stop the World," pages 76–78).

Where to Aim the Camera

Because you will mostly photograph the Zodiac, you can clamp the camera on a tripod and aim it exactly as you would point your Starframe on the identical culmination dates and times. They are all given in this book along with elevation angles. You may be working almost in the dark when you start photography, but like astronauts who navigate with similar bearings, you will be on target even if you can barely see your anchor stars through the viewfinder. Your film emulsion will capture them for you, along with all the pictogram stars. Just try it and see. Once you have loaded your camera with new ISO 400, 800, 1000, or even faster film,[1] mount it securely on a clamp or tripod. You will need a *cable release* to open and close your shutter without shaking the camera.

* * * * * * * * *

[1] Ask the salesperson in a reputable camera store for film information; also ask about "pushing" film to make it even more sensitive.

How to Set the Camera

There are many different kinds of 35mm single-lens reflex cameras. Twenty years ago, the cable release was pressed between thumb and forefinger to open the shutter without shaking the camera on the tripod. Today you can press a button on a cable that will hold the lens open for you for a preset time interval. Expensive models can even imprint—right on your film—the exact date and time when your exposures were actually taken. Very expensive camera systems can be programmed to take your pictures at night while you sleep. If you own such an electronic camera be sure to set it on "manual operation" for astrophotography, to start.

Camera basics have not changed and are not likely to change. They consist of the following:

Focus:

To shoot stars, you do *not* need automatic focusing. All stars are "infinitely" far away for photographic purposes, which is why you should set the lens *always at infinity,* marked with this symbol: ∞.

Aperture:

In keeping with the concept of speed, where your lens serves as the patient eye that can collect starlight over seconds or minutes (even hours) of time, your lens aperture setting, to start, should be *always wide open.* That may be f/1.4, f/1.8, or f/2. There is an aperture illustration in "Adapting to the Dark" (see page 130).

Exposure:

Since, at least for the beginning, exposure time is the only variable with which you can, or will want to, experiment under the night sky, the exposure setting should be *always on "bulb"* (sometimes marked with a *B*). Thus you can select the length of any exposure, take it, then write it down in your notebook. Otherwise, you will never remember how long an exposure was on frame 18 of your third film roll.

To develop valuable *empirical information* (information based on your own experience) in your notebook, you should start with the number of the roll of film (noting its type and speed). Then continue by listing each individual frame or picture: what you photographed, the camera settings, exposure times, dates, starting and ending times, and notes.

It was during a search for meteors that I took my most important series of photographic records on frames 16 through 29 of a roll of black-and-white Tri-X film on my 166th roll. On the night of August 28–29 in 1975, while my home-built automatic camera was aimed at the constellation Cygnus, I recorded thirteen photographs of a nova exploding in the starfield of the Swan. This is an unprecedented prediscovery sequence of pictures (see illustration 15) which was taken before the nova was even discovered in Japan, a day later.

Because the automatic programmable cameras of today were not yet available in 1975, I had built a "Rube Goldberg" device. My single-lens reflex was activated, and the film was advanced by a lawn-sprinkler timer, an erector-set pulley, and some monofilament line.

If I had known of the "blinking rabbit discovery" (see pages 84–86), I would today also be able to claim the discovery of Nova Cygni 1975. As it is, I remain the only person, professional or amateur, who ever photographed the birth of a nova actually occurring in sequential pictures. My log clearly states that these important photographs (they were analyzed by the Smithsonian Astrophysical Observatory at Harvard University) were taken from the roof of my house in West Los Angeles.

Project Scorpius

It is impossible to view the ancient constellation of the celestial Scorpion without mentioning the starfield Libra. Scorpius lies close to Libra, adjoining it. Until Roman times the two regions were one, as described in "Project Libra" (see pages 63–67). They formed one of the most extended of the original six sections of the Zodiac. The names given to this starfield ranged from Scorpios to Scorpius, but it is often called Scorpio, the name given to it by Astrologers. The pictogram shape reminds us of the order of insects to which the scorpion belongs, with its crablike claws and the venomous stinger at the end of its curved tail.

The brightest star in Scorpius has already been mentioned, and perhaps viewed, in connection with Libra. It is the extra-bright, reddish, first-magnitude star called Antares. Like most first-magnitude stars, it is also known by its Greek letter in combination with the possessive form of the name of the constellation. You may want to call Antares Alpha (**α**) Scorpii. We have spoken of the similarity in magnitude and color between this Alpha star and the planet Mars. The Greek name Antares actually translates into "rival of Mars," stressing the likeness of the two.

The constellation Scorpius lies far south, low in the sky. You will find it barely one Starframe above the southern horizon. Look for it just above the southern compass point (see illustration 16). In far northern states and latitudes the star Antares itself will be readily visible, although portions of the curved tail—perhaps even the "stinger"—may either be just touching the southern horizon or be hidden below it.

Fortunately, there are enough bright anchor stars in the triangular head of the Scorpion, with Akrab, Beta (**β**) in Scorpius, and Dschubba, Delta (**δ**) in Scorpius, both at second magnitude. This allows you to align the Starframe easily and turn it into correct position when holding it 15–18 inches from the eye.

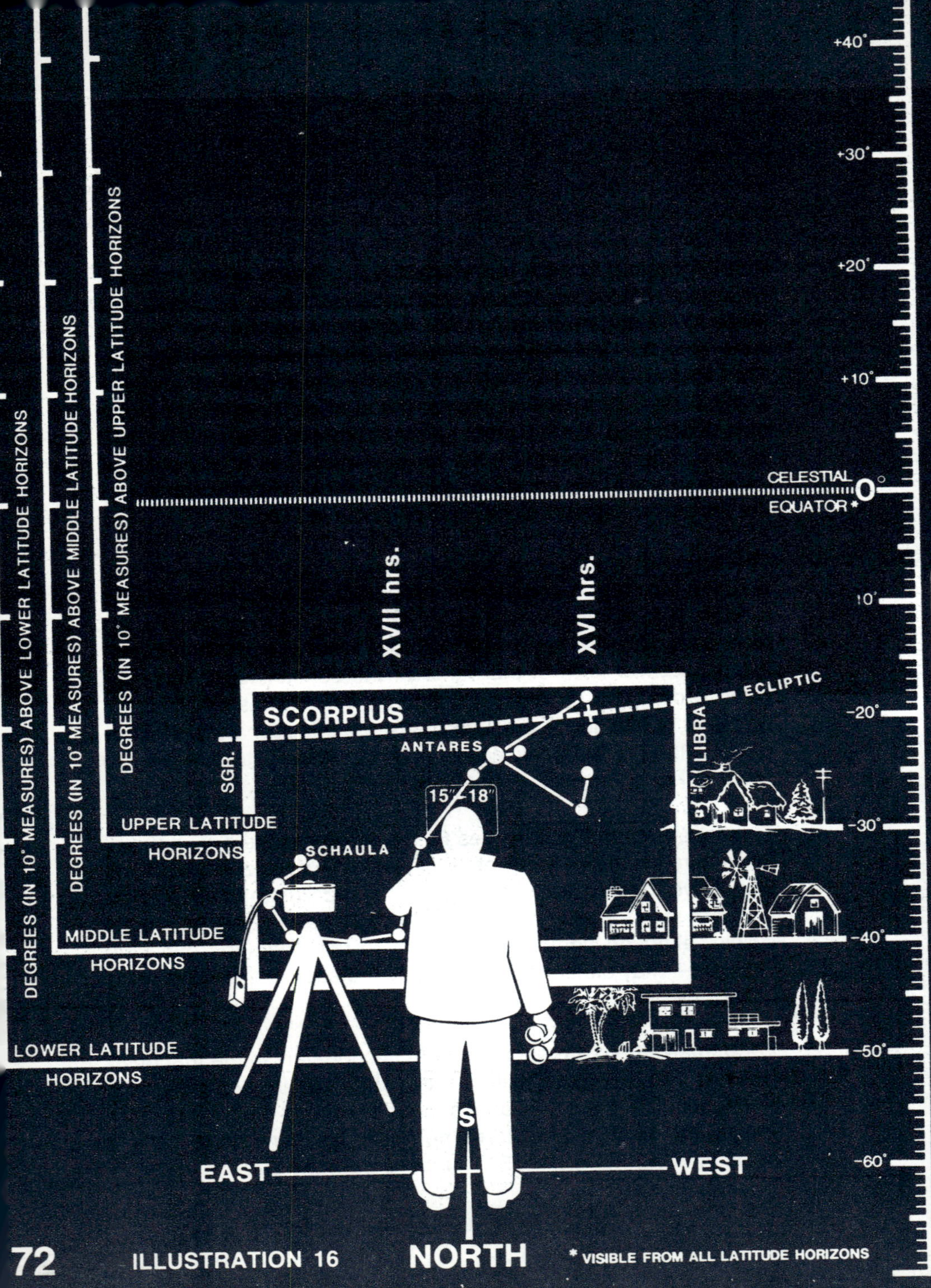

ILLUSTRATION 16

CULMINATIONS OF THE SCORPIUS STARFIELD
(see illustration on left)

Hold the Starframe 15–18 inches from the eye

March 15-April 1	at 5:00 am	= 05:00 hours
*April 1-April 15	at 5:00 am	= 05:00 hours
*April 15-May 1	at 4:00 am	= 04:00 hours
*May 1-May 15	at 3:00 am	= 03:00 hours
*May 15-June 1	at 2:00 am	= 02:00 hours
*June 1-June 15	at 1:00 am	= 01:00 hours
*June 15-July 1	at MIDNIGHT	= 24:00 hours
*July 1-July 15	at 11:00 pm	= 23:00 hours
*July 15-August 1	at 10:00 pm	= 22:00 hours
*August 1-August 15	at 9:00 pm	= 21:00 hours
*August 15-September 1	at 8:00 pm	= 20:00 hours
*September 1-September 15	at 7:00 pm	= 19:00 hours

*Times on these dates are adjusted for daylight saving time.

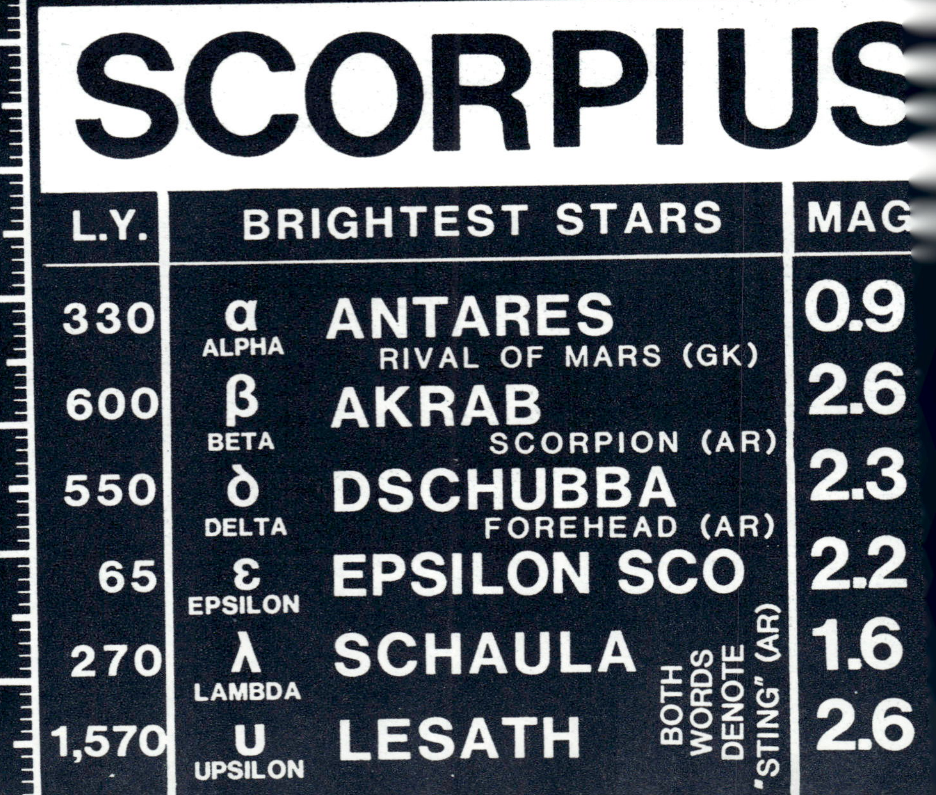

SCORPIUS

L.Y.	BRIGHTEST STARS		MAG
330	α ALPHA	ANTARES RIVAL OF MARS (GK)	0.9
600	β BETA	AKRAB SCORPION (AR)	2.6
550	δ DELTA	DSCHUBBA FOREHEAD (AR)	2.3
65	ε EPSILON	EPSILON SCO	2.2
270	λ LAMBDA	SCHAULA	1.6
1,570	υ UPSILON	LESATH	2.6

BOTH WORDS DENOTE "STING" (AR)

Observers in southern states and latitudes will easily be able to see the second-brightest star in the region and a nearby companion star, marking the stinger of the Scorpion. Its Arabic name, Schaula, actually means "sting." This Lambda (λ) star is of magnitude 1.6. Antares and Schaula between them show the angular width and height of the entire constellation of Scorpius, conveniently filling a Starframe.

Look for the galactic clusters M6 and M7. Under black skies, they will reveal themselves as hazy patches to the naked eye. A pair of binoculars can separate some of the individual stars in these "open" stargroupings. M4, a *globular cluster,* may seem like a "fuzzy" star of sixth magnitude. Such globulars contain thousands, even hundreds of thousands, of stars, all packed tightly together in a ball-shaped configuration. (See back cover.)

In other cultures too, Scorpius has long been included as one of the major constellations. Thus it was called Tsing Lung, the "azure dragon," in one of the four great divisions of the Chinese Zodiac.

An important scientific fact should be emphasized here: it is that the sun can be seen and confirmed in the constellation Scorpius for only seven days in each year, approximately from November 22–30. Then, *before* journeying into Sagittarius, the Archer, the sun will travel through the southern region of the starfield called Ophiuchus, the Serpent Bearer. It will dwell in this constellation, known since earliest Greek astronomy, from about November 30 until December 17. When astrology was first put to arcane uses thousands of years ago, the sun missed this ancient constellation, also known as the Snake Carrier. Today, however, due to the formal redefinition of constellation boundaries by the I.A.U. (the International Astronomical Union), the sun spends twice as much time in the adjacent Serpent Bearer as in the celebrated Scorpion. Because such information might impair or undermine the astrological beliefs of "inhabitants" of the signs of the Scorpion and the Archer, it is not played up here.

Precession also (see page 23) has moved most Scorpios squarely into the domain of Libra in the twentieth century. This imperceptible motion has transported many who believed themselves to be inhabitants of one constellation into another. (See chart on page 28.) Precession was first observed two thousand years ago by Hipparchus, the Greek astrologer-astronomer. Inevitably, and in time, it will lead to a re-evaluation of the Sun signs and a new "observational astrology."

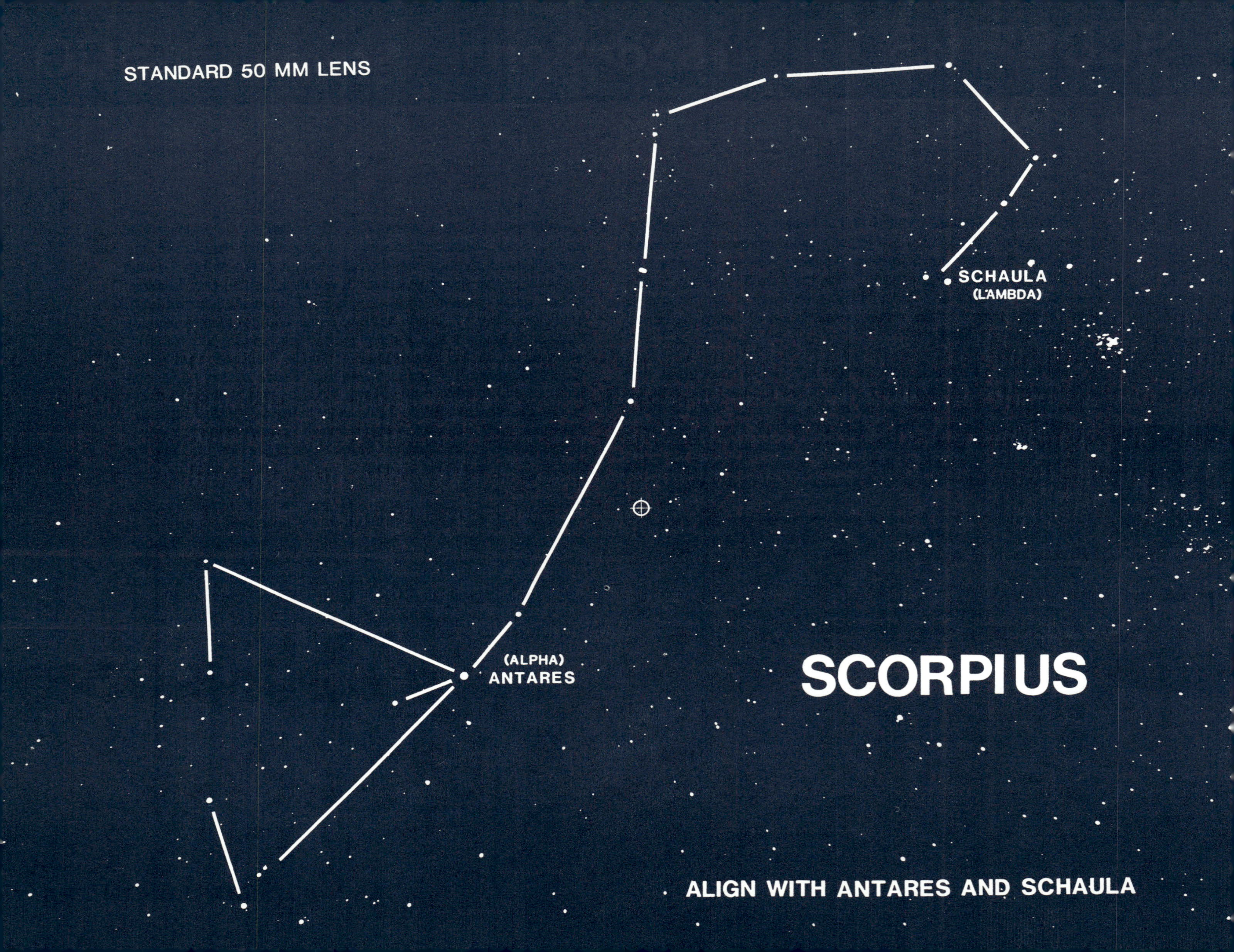

STANDARD 50 MM LENS

SCHAULA
(LAMBDA)

(ALPHA)
ANTARES

SCORPIUS

ALIGN WITH ANTARES AND SCHAULA

OPHIUCHUS

ECLIPTIC

PATH OF THE SUN IN NOVEMBER

SCORPIUS

LIBRA

M80

ANTARES α

M4

-30°

M6

M7

SAGITTARIUS

SCHAULA λ

ALIGN WITH ANTARES AND SCHAULA

16h

Stop the World

You may not be interested in "stopping the world" until you have taken your first roll of sky photographs. The difference between any short 15-second or 30-second exposures (take several of each) and the long 2-minute or 4-minute exposures (again, take several) will instantly give you good reason to try. Please take accurate notes.

If you have followed the simple instructions for aiming your tripod-mounted camera just like your Starframes, at the culmination dates and times, then your chosen constellation will be in your pictures. If you heeded camera settings, kept light away from your lens, and did not shake or move the tripod or SLR, you should have two kinds of photographs without any trouble.

The short (15–30-second) exposures will show star*dots* that are nearly round and starlike. You can compare them with the star-charts in this book. The longer (2- or 4-minute) pictures will show star*trails* that reveal the length of the time that the shutter was held open. If you caught a shooting star, it will engrave its momentary light streak on the emulsion of the film for a record, regardless of the length of the exposure (see illustration 17).

To collect more starlight and ever more faint *round* star images, it is obvious that you want to be able to hold the shutter open for 2, 4, or even 8 minutes to produce pictures like the right ones in our pairs of starmaps. You can do away with the trails caused by the rotation of our planet on its axis by "stopping the earth from moving." It stands to reason that any motor drive mechanism designed to turn a camera in step with the stars will arrest their apparent trailing motion. Such a system should turn in a westward direction, opposite to the rotation of our earth. It should revolve once in 24 hours. This will allow photography of much fainter stars and objects because—quite literally—the imperceptible motion of the earth will no longer "pull" the camera and film out from beneath the star during exposures.

Small motors that turn at 1/24 R.P.H. (revolutions per hour), which equals one revolution per 24-hour day, are available in the marketplace.[1] A reasonably priced synchronous-type motor with its small 1/8-inch-diameter drive shaft, when mounted parallel to the axis of our planet, is all that will be required to "stop the world." A *STELAS* will literally seem to *S*top *T*he *E*arth, *L*ock *A*ll *S*tars (see illustration 18). Once we mount the accumulator of starlight on a

NORTH STAR REGION PHOTOGRAPH.
FILM: KODAK TRI-X PAN, ISO 400.
EXPOSURE: 60 MINUTES.
APERTURE: f/4 STANDARD LENS.
GOOD TARGET FOR METEOR SHOWERS.

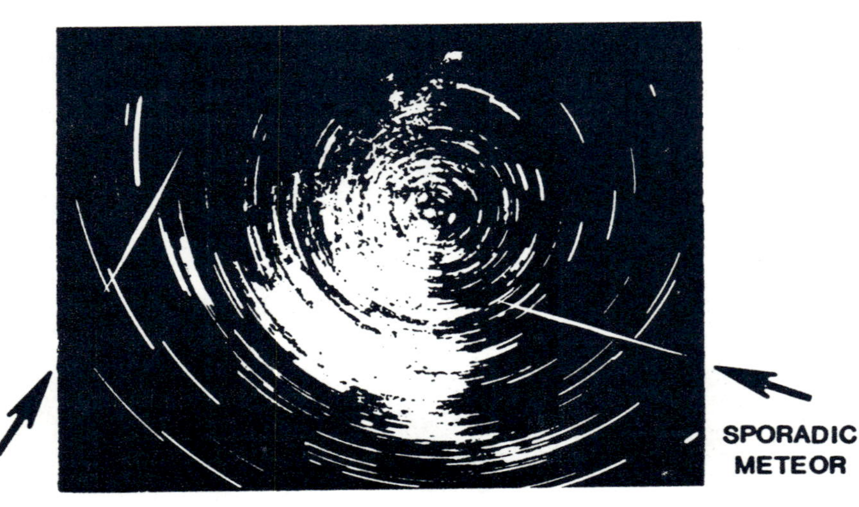

ILLUSTRATION 17

[1] Model 3941 available from ORION TELESCOPE CENTER, 421 Soquel Avenue, Santa Cruz, California 95062; Telephone (408)458-9090.

A▸ STELASCOPE ALIGNER
1/4" DIAMETER DRINKING STRAW 6" LONG

B▸ EQUATORIAL DRIVE MOTOR
1/24 REVOLUTION PER HOUR

C▸ MOTOR SUPPORT BLOCK
3/4" PLYWOOD 2 1/4" X 3"

D▸ MAIN SUPPORT BLOCK
3/4" PLYWOOD 4" X 3"

E▸ TEE NUT
1/4" RECESSED 3/8" FROM TOP SURFACE

F▸ ATTACHMENT TO TRIPOD
1/4" TRIPOD SCREW INSERTED HERE

G▸ THRUST (SUPPORT) BEARINGS
SCREEN DOOR ROLLERS (PAIR)

H▸ CONNECTOR-PLATE
GEAR BLANK WITH 1.250 BORE

J▸ CAMERA BALL HEAD
DOT LINE CORP. ITEM DL-0609

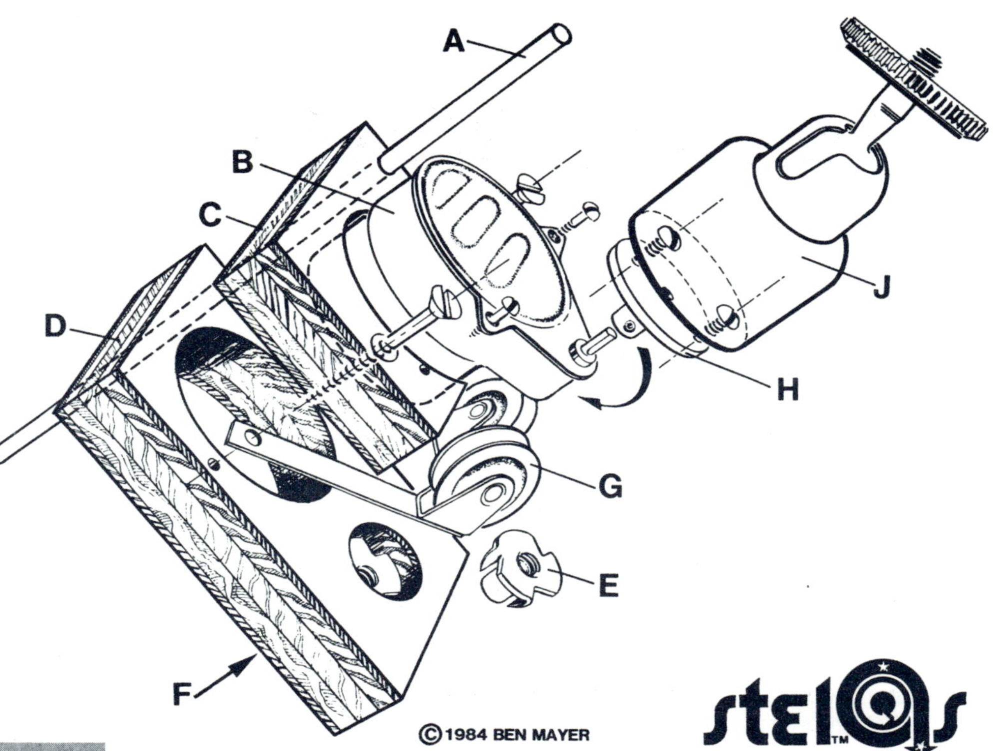

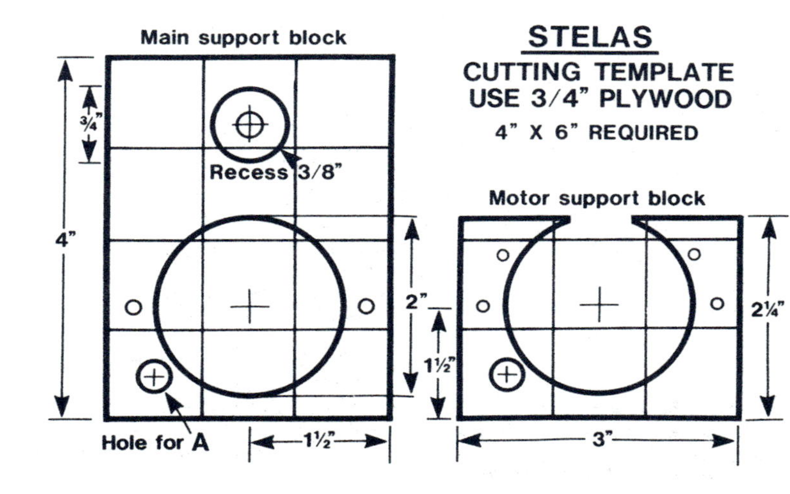

ILLUSTRATION 18

photographic ball socket (Item J), we can point our single-lens reflex camera anywhere in the sky. Now we are ready for much longer exposures.

Even the most preliminary test will show the tremendous difference in results that will be achieved by lengthening the "undriven" 15-second exposure to a "driven" 30 seconds or redoubling that to 1 minute. Once you expose with a STELAS for 2 minutes or longer, you are well into advanced astrophotography. Longer "driven" exposures will catch so much more starlight that you may want to experiment with smaller aperture settings, trying f/2 or even f/2.8. This will result in sharper pictures and crisper star images. Your pictures will not only surprise you, they will defy belief among your friends. They can equal any starcharts printed in these pages.

A word of caution: The STELAS drive system has been tested and works extremely well. But as can be surmised from looking at illustration 18, a considerable load is being brought to bear on the small drive shaft of the motor with the weight of the camera. Do not attempt to use heavier cameras with slower zoom or telephoto lenses. The STELAS works best with any standard 35mm SLR with a 50mm lens. Do not overload this simple system or its motor.

It is easy to find Polaris, the North Star, also known as the Pole star. It is the star most nearly above our North Pole. You will not even need a Stellaphane; a simple Starframe will do. This easy search can be conducted anywhere in the Northern Hemisphere at any time, on any date in the year.

The compass will come in handy, because for once you must stand facing north. Depending on where you live, hold your Starframe pointing it due north at 45 degrees above the *northern* horizon from Maine, or at 30 degrees above it from Florida.

Northern ancients knew Polaris well and sailed their ships by its position. It is always in the nightsky, anytime at all. When the Starframe is pointed correctly, the North Pole star will be the brightest in the middle of your viewfinder. Not a dazzling object, but easily visible at magnitude two. No need to worry about planets this far north of the Zodiac. There will be none to confuse you. At +90 degrees, you will be looking at the Alpha (**α**) Ursa Minoris star in the constellation, the Little Dipper, of which Polaris forms a part. To align the STELAS correctly, sight the drinking straw (Item A) on Polaris. Then take a 60-minute exposure at any hour, anytime of the year, stopping down the lens to the f/4 setting. (see illustration 17). It might surprise you!

Good telescopes (see "Resources," page 135) come equipped with built-in *equatorial drives.* Unquestionably, this motor capability is their most valuable and important feature. To utilize it for basic star photography you only need attach your camera piggyback *on top* of your telescope, following the manufacturer's instructions. (See illustration 27.)

Often, irresponsible advertisements show telescopes with cameras attached to the eyepiece position. It is only natural for the lay person to think that it is easy to photograph even Messier objects in this manner, but no: one can take telescopic pictures of brightly lit distant sailboats on a sunny day, and even record the full moon (see pages 54–55) *through* a telescope. But to utilize the most important feature of such systems, one should begin to use the barrel of the 'scope merely as a "driven" tripod, to photograph the twelve zodiacal constellations. Soon other splendid starfields will beckon.

You will have come a long way from Babylonian ziggurats once Polaris becomes your anchor star.

Project Sagittarius

Eastward from Scorpius lies what may be viewed as the richest starfield in the celestial sphere. It is the region of Sagittarius. In history, it was first regarded as a minotaur and later as a centaur, half man and half animal. Since both are mythological figures based on ancient Greek legends, human interpretations of any visual images are, at best, speculation. Has anyone ever seen such a creature? But even city dwellers can readily see a "teapot" pictogram in Sagittarius instead of the imaginary bow-and-arrowed Archer. The constellation lies about one Starframe above the southern compass point, about 15–30 degrees above the horizon.

As always, for the culmination of constellations, you should stand facing due south with your back to the north. Check your orientation with a compass by the faint light of a red-shielded flashlight. The Starframe must be the standard distance of 15–18 inches from your eye.

From astronomical studies of globular clusters and the more open galactic clusters, we have been able to establish that our solar system, with its planets, lies rather "far out." It is located near the perimeter of our saucer-shaped Milky Way galaxy. The center of our island universe lies in the direction of Sagittarius. The Milky Way appears most dazzling in the region of our galactic center.

A trip away from city lights during warm summer nights can be a truly rewarding experience. An overnight camp-out in sleeping bags will be an unforgettable adventure for youngsters. It offers an opportunity to bring home the awareness of our place in the sun and among the stars. Dress warmly—it does get chilly at night and cold before dawn. Try to take a camera, tripod, and one roll of fast film to fill with starlight (see "Shooting Shooting Stars," pages 68–70).

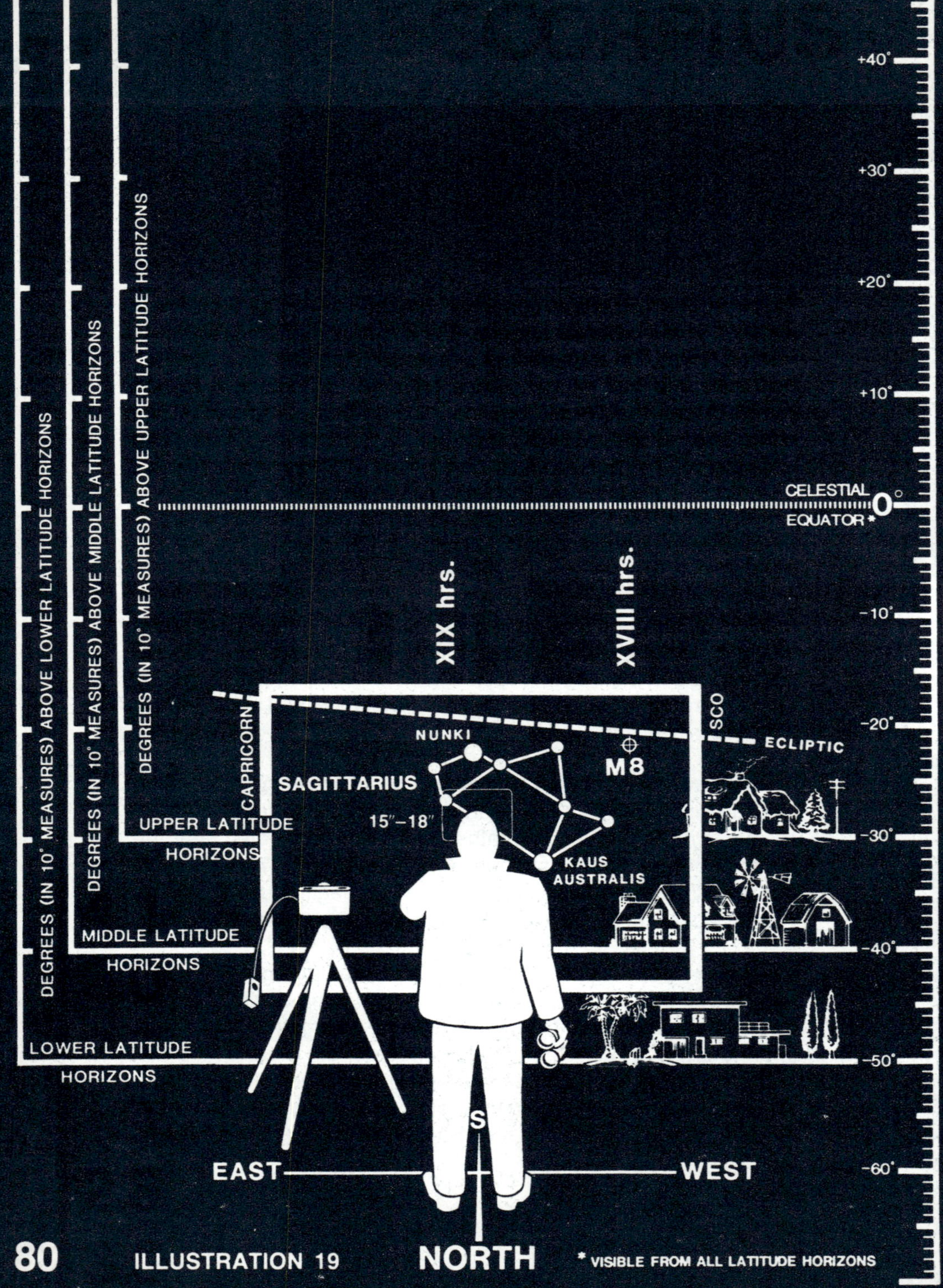

ILLUSTRATION 19

* VISIBLE FROM ALL LATITUDE HORIZONS

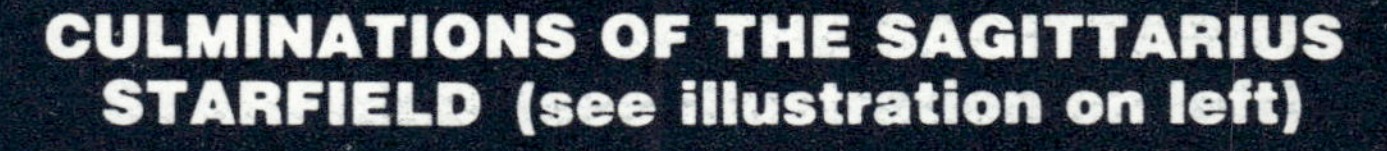

CULMINATIONS OF THE SAGITTARIUS STARFIELD (see illustration on left)

Hold the Starframe 15–18 inches from eye

*May 1-May 15	at 5:00 am	=	05:00 hours
*May 15-June 1	at 4:00 am	=	04:00 hours
*June 1-June 15	at 3:00 am	=	03:00 hours
*June 15-July 1	at 2:00 am	=	02:00 hours
*July 1-July 15	at 1:00 am	=	01:00 hours
*July 15-August 1	at MIDNIGHT	=	24:00 hours
*August 1-August 15	at 11:00 pm	=	23:00 hours
*August 15-September 1	at 10:00 pm	=	22:00 hours
*September 1-September 15	at 9:00 pm	=	21:00 hours
*September 15-October 1	at 8:00 pm	=	20:00 hours
*October 1-October 15	at 7:00 pm	=	19:00 hours

*Times on these dates adjusted for daylight saving time.

SAGITTARIUS

L.Y.	BRIGHTEST STARS	MAG.
210	σ SIGMA NUNKI (BABYLONIAN)	2.0
250	α ALPHA RUKBAT KNEE OF THE ARCHER (AR)	4.1
120	γ GAMMA AL NASL THE ARROWHEAD (AR)	3.0
82	δ DELTA KAUS MERIDIONALIS MIDDLE BOWSTAR	2.7
85	ε EPSILON KAUS AUSTRALIS SOUTHERN BOWSTAR	1.9
98	λ LAMBDA KAUS BOREALIS NORTHERN BOWSTAR	2.8
78	ζ ZETA ASCELLA ARMPIT (LATIN)	3.0

In most constellations the Alpha or Beta stars are usually the brightest. Not in Sagittarius. Here Sigma (σ) Sagittarii, called Nunki, with Epsilon (ε) Sagittarii, called Kaus Australis, share the honor. Nunki forms the top of the handle of the teapot and Gamma (γ) Sagittarii the front of the spout. The Gamma star, literally called "Al Nasl, "the arrowhead," marks the tip of the allegorical arrow. Together with Delta (δ) Sagittarii, called Kaus Meridionalis, which translates as "the middle bowstar," the line from Gamma to Delta forms the arrow, the last reminder of the ancient celebrated archer and his bow.

M8, the famous Lagoon Nebula, lies just above the spout of the teapot. It forms one of the brightest treasures in Sagittarius. In color photographs it reveals vast clouds of pink hydrogen gas that mark this swirling region (see back cover). It is generally believed to be a birthplace of new stars. The famous Trifid Nebula, called M20 in Charles Messier's list, lies to the north of the Lagoon by only two angular degrees. Under good dark skies, you may find these nebulae even with binoculars. Both objects lie about twenty-five hundred light years away. This means that when their light embarked on its journey to us, the Parthenon in Athens, Greece, had just been built and stood atop the Acropolis, new and unblemished in perfect marble splendor.

M22 and M55 are globular clusters. They are of similar apparent brightness and will appear as sixth-magnitude stars to the naked eye or camera. They are ten thousand and twenty thousand light years away from earth. The variable stars R, W, and RR will be within your reach. There are about twenty-three hundred variables in this constellation alone. Many require powerful telescopes and sensitive photometers to record their changes in magnitude.

During dark nights, the countless stars of the center of our galaxy seem to rise like steam from the spout of a kettle over the front of the teapot. Together these stars appear like an endless, dense cloud. They are too plentiful to be seen or distinguished individually.

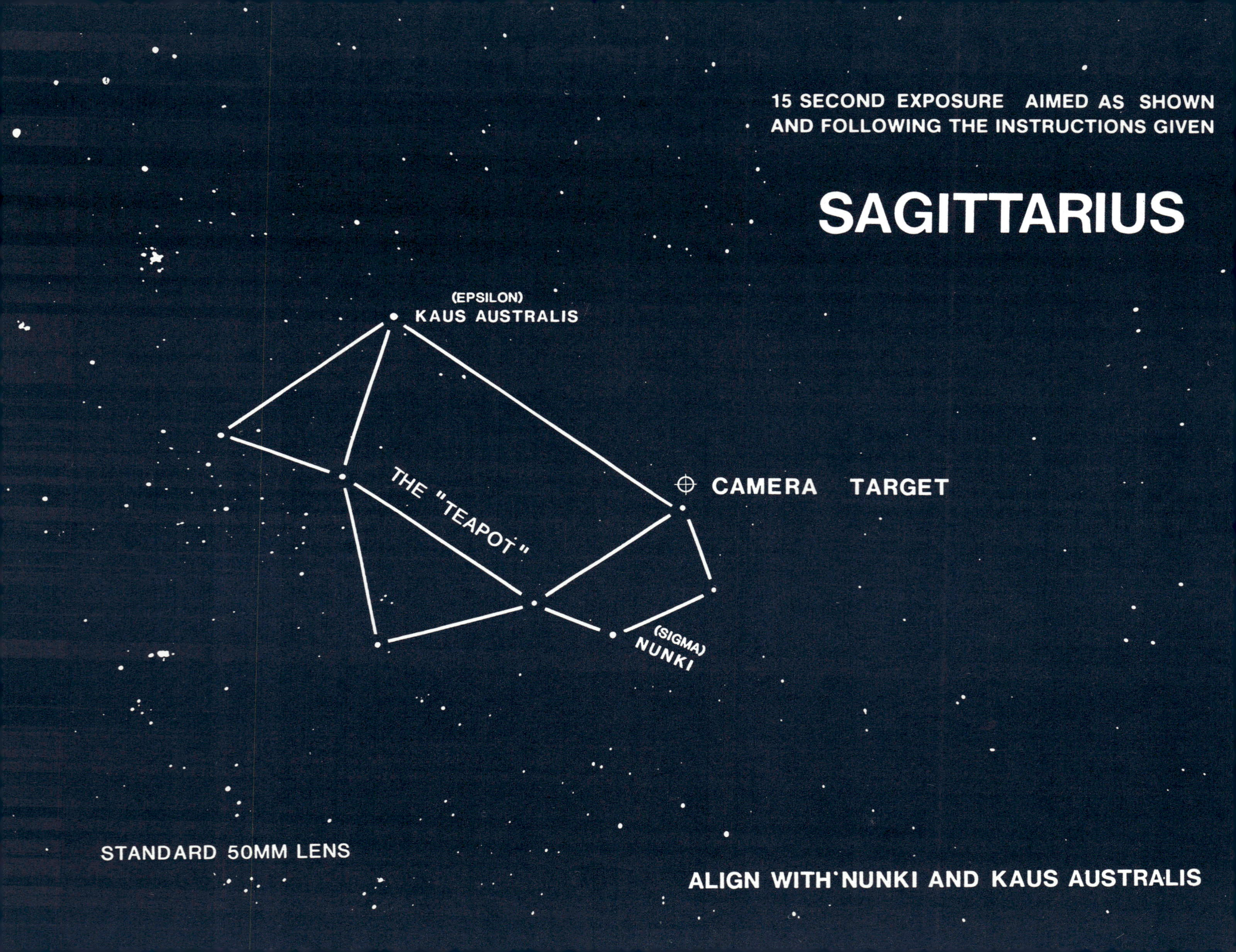

15 SECOND EXPOSURE AIMED AS SHOWN
AND FOLLOWING THE INSTRUCTIONS GIVEN

SAGITTARIUS

(EPSILON)
KAUS AUSTRALIS

THE "TEAPOT"

CAMERA TARGET

(SIGMA)
NUNKI

STANDARD 50MM LENS

ALIGN WITH NUNKI AND KAUS AUSTRALIS

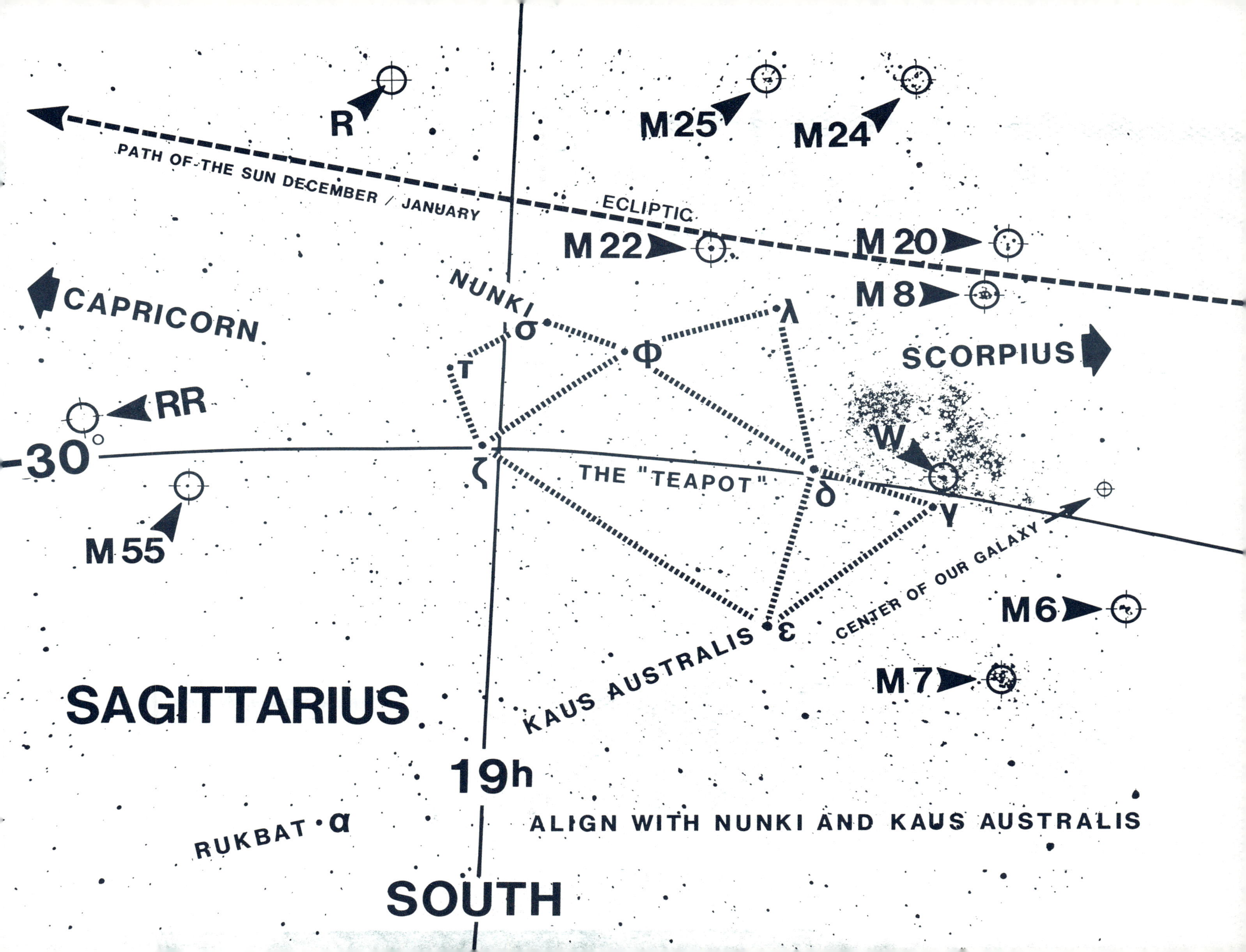
R
M25
M24
PATH OF THE SUN DECEMBER / JANUARY
ECLIPTIC
M22
M20
M8
NUNKI
CAPRICORN
σ
λ
Φ
SCORPIUS
τ
RR
W
-30°
ζ
THE "TEAPOT"
δ
γ
M55
CENTER OF OUR GALAXY
M6
ε
KAUS AUSTRALIS
M7
SAGITTARIUS
19h
RUKBAT α
ALIGN WITH NUNKI AND KAUS AUSTRALIS
SOUTH

The Blinking Rabbit Discovery

One of the most important reasons to encourage the universal collecting of starlight with simple photography is the chance for "Eureka" discoveries (see "Shooting Shooting Stars," pages 68–70). The mere taking of star pictures, even those containing flashing meteors, will not of itself hold your interest, except for the novelty of being able to document any constellations of your choice for a permanent record. One must think of photography as an important basic step toward discovery, the possible revelation of something never before seen by anyone, anywhere. It can open the road to scientific fame.

The height of this thrill came to starlover Clyde Tombaugh on February 18, 1930, when he became the discoverer of planet X, later to be named Pluto. The methods used were identical to the ones that will be explained here. Young Tombaugh discovered Pluto, not at night, but "on a cloudy day, close to four o'clock in the afternoon."[1] He spotted it not through the eyepiece of a telescope, because he made his historic find with a *blinking device* while comparing two negatives of Gemini photographs he had taken on January 21 and 23. (On negative films, stardots appear as black spots on a clear background, as seen in all starcharts on the right-hand pages.)

Pluto became one of the major astronomical finds of this century. It parallels in importance the discovery of the supernova that exploded in 1987, again to be first seen in a photograph, this time taken by a Canadian in the Southern Hemisphere. My friend Bill Liller, coauthor of the *Cambridge Astronomy Guide*[2], uses a basic SLR camera and has to date made five nova discoveries using a *Steblicom* (see page 92), a home-built blinking discovery device.

. . . .

[1] Clyde Tombaugh and Patrick Moore, *Out of the Darkness: The Planet Pluto.* Harrisburg, Pennsylvania: Stackpole Books, 1980.

[2] William Liller and Ben Mayer, *The Cambridge Astronomy Guide: An Introduction to Practical Astronomy.* Cambridge, England: Cambridge University Press, 1985.

ILLUSTRATION 20

Reference Image (Before)

ILLUSTRATION 21

Data Image (After)

When I recently addressed the American Astronomical League, I tried to help the audience visualize what "blinking" is all about. Two ordinary slide projectors assembled into a *PROBLICOM* (*PRO*jection *BLI*nk *COM*parator) (see illustration 24), and a pair of slides would have demonstrated visually what I tried to explain with the analogy of the blinking rabbit discovery:

> It is daytime. Two persons are viewing a field with sparse trees standing among stones and pebbles. There's a brook in the middle distance.
>
> "I'll take a picture," says Shawn, and as he focuses the camera he adds: "I see a rabbit sitting upright over there." He clicks the shutter (see illustration 20).
>
> "Where?" asks Heather. "I can't see it."
>
> "It's difficult to notice," says Shawn. "It blends into the surroundings."
>
> At that moment the rabbit takes one hop forward, giving away its position.
>
> "I see it now!" exclaims Heather, who had been looking in the right direction but needed the revealing motion to discover the well-camouflaged creature.
>
> "Let me take another picture," Shawn says. "Then I can 'blink' the pair and reveal the rabbit with its motion." He snaps a second photograph (see illustration 21). "Now people with stereovision (stereopsis) will be able to find the rabbit by just looking—sort of focusing—between the two pictures or 'blinking' the slides."

If you change the scene to nighttime, turn the stony field into the starry skies and the rabbit into a planet, you quickly begin to visualize what makes "blinking" into such an easy and powerful discovery process. This elegant method came into use with the invention of photography, without which comparison blinking would never have come into its own. It is an excellent yet simple way to show "before" and "after" situations, which in astronomy can lead to critical discoveries. The more people participate in the endeavor, the greater our chance for understanding the sky. To start we can begin finding the planets in zodiacal constellations as they reveal themselves through their motion.

You do not have to photograph the rabbit during the moment when it actually makes its revealing hop. That would be too sudden and difficult to anticipate. *Clyde Tombaugh did not even know where the faint planet X might be roaming.* It is only necessary to have a "before" photograph to compare with an "after" photograph to place yourself on the threshold of meaningful astronomical discovery.

You may not even know it, but one of the very first photographs you took to test different exposures may contain a celestial wanderer. If you kept good notes on just what you did, what film you used, and how long your exposures were, you may be able to reshoot that constellation tonight. Then you have two images for comparison with a blinking device. A moving object—all other stars will stay quite still—will most probably be one of our planets revealing itself through its motion.

Then again, if you photographed under dark skies, with the camera mounted on a STELAS drive motor for a long exposure, (see "Stop the World," pages 76–78), the blinking object might be a planet, an asteroid (a small planetoid), or, just conceivably, a comet—perhaps one never seen before. In that case, your photographs will become the discovery images of a comet that will bear your own name. For as long as humankind continues to keep astronomical records, your discovery will be remembered in the log of Genesis time.

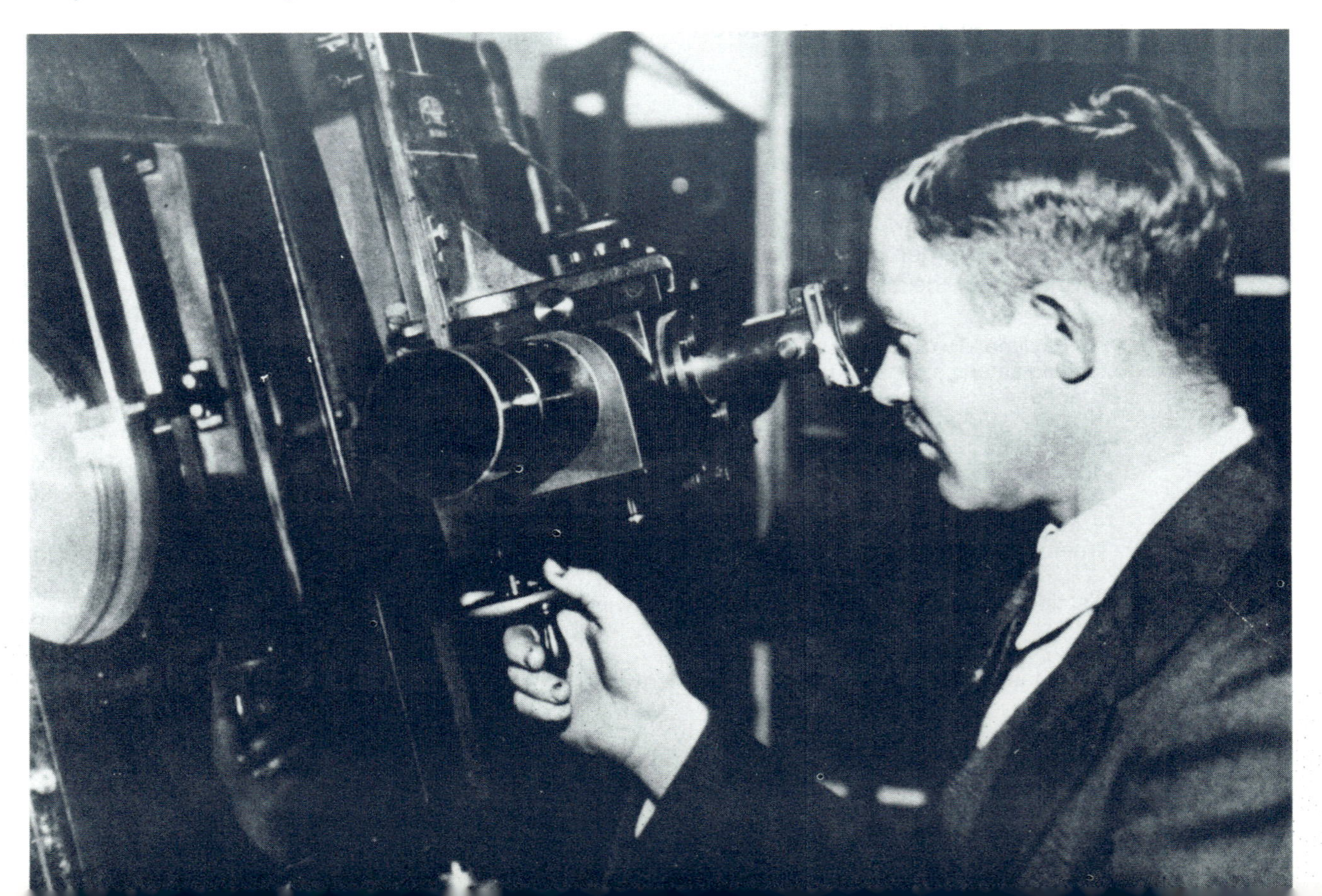

Clyde Tombaugh in 1938 at the Zeiss blink microscope where he spent more than seven thousand hours.

Project Capricorn

The constellation Capricorn was already known in ancient Babylon. Its name, the Goatfish, relates to legends that have their origins in Greek mythology. The fish aspect connects Capricorn with the following two constellations of Aquarius and Pisces. Here begins the region that was called "water-filled" by the ancients. It was referred to as "the celestial sea." Other constellations that lie nearby tell the story: the Dolphin, the Whale, and the Southern Fish.

The pictogram of Capricorn looks more like the bottom part of an abbreviated bikini swimsuit than anything else. Modesty may be what makes it difficult to find.

Because it can be difficult to see in light-polluted areas, you may want to find Capricorn with some simple 15-second-exposure photographs (see "Shooting Shooting Stars," pages 68–70). Aim your Starframe and/or your camera 20 degrees above the southern compass point. To improve the chances at your latitude and to discover the easy-to-recognize pictogram, try several pictures at different elevation angles. Estimate 30 degrees, 20 degrees, and then 10 degrees above the southern horizon. Don't forget, the Starframe measures 30 degrees in its narrow dimension when held 15–18 inches from your eye. You may not be able to see spots of light through the viewfinder of your camera unless a planet is paying a visit to the Goatfish, but you will catch your quarry, for sure.

So reliable and unfailing are the stars in the heavens that one can predict with absolute certainty that, weather permitting, you will succeed in your search. This method will work anywhere, for any constellation, if dates, times, and instructions, as listed above, are observed. Moonlight should always be avoided during the brief moments needed to obtain pictograms with a camera, but other unavoidable light pollution may be overcome.

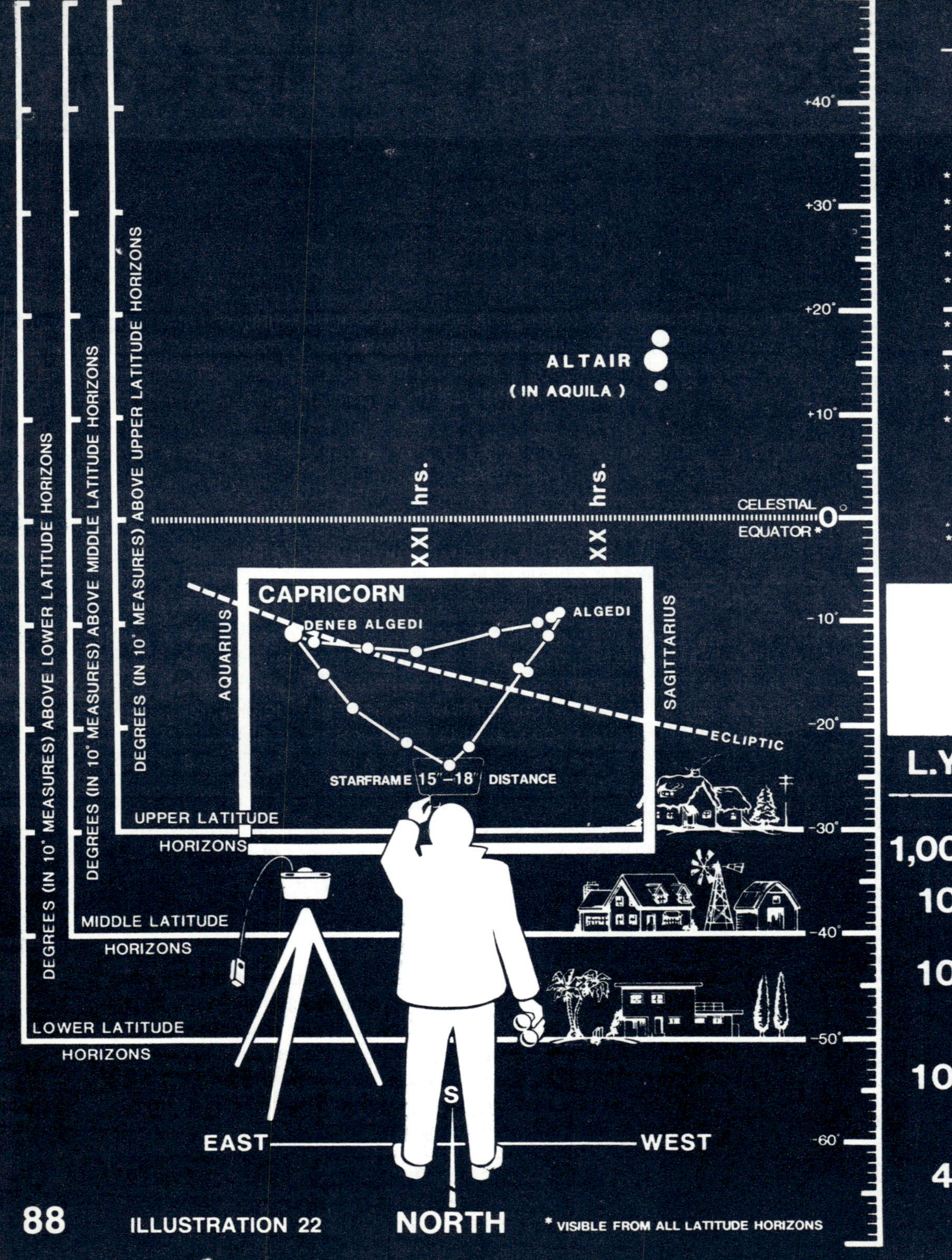

ILLUSTRATION 22

CULMINATIONS OF THE CAPRICORN STARFIELD (see illustration on left)

Hold the Starframe 15–18 inches from eye

*June 1-June 15	at 5:00 am	= 05:00 hours
*June 15-July 1	at 4:00 am	= 04:00 hours
*July 1-July 15	at 3:00 am	= 03:00 hours
*July 15-August 1	at 2:00 am	= 02:00 hours
*August 1-August 15	at 1:00 am	= 01:00 hours
*August 15-September 1	at MIDNIGHT	= 24:00 hours
*September 1-September 15	at 11:00 pm	= 23:00 hours
*September 15-October 1	at 10:00 pm	= 22:00 hours
*October 1-October 15	at 9:00 pm	= 21:00 hours
October 15-November 1	at 7:00 pm	= 19:00 hours

(Pls. note that between October 15 and November 1, we "fall" back 1 hour), setting our clocks back to standard time.

*Times on these dates are adjusted for daylight saving time.

CAPRICORN

L.Y.	BRIGHTEST STARS	MAG
1,000	α_1 ALGEDI THE GOAT (AR)	4.2
100	α_2 ALPHA	3.6
100	β BETA DABIH SLAUGHTERER'S STAR (AR)	3.1
100	γ GAMMA NASHIRA GOOD TIDINGS STAR (AR)	3.8
49	δ DELTA DENEB ALGEDI TAIL OF THE GOAT (AR)	2.9

In photographs, as in the sky, the brightest star here will be Delta (δ) Capricorni, named Deneb Algedi. This literally translates into "the tail of the goat." Its magnitude is 2.9. The Alpha stars—and there are two of them very close together, Alpha 1 (α_1) and Alpha 2 (α_2)—are fittingly called Algedi, meaning "the goat." Their magnitudes of 4.2 and 3.6, respectively, may together make them appear brighter than the Delta (δ) star. To the naked eye the pair may look like one object.

In our starchart photographs, the elongated image of Algedi hints at the double nature of this star. Only telescopes can reveal that both of these stars are in themselves double stars again. Alpha 1 (α_1) can be separated into two individual suns of magnitudes 4.5 and 9.0. Alpha 2 (α_2) can be "split" into separate stars of 3.6 and 10.6. This is a "double double."

The fainter Capricorn doubles are also called *binary stars* and revolve around their common centers of gravity. They perform an unending minuet, with the two partners whirling tirelessly about each other in space. The rapture of the depth of the universe may be felt when we learn from astronomy that Alpha 2 (α_2) in Capricorn is 100 light years away from us, while Alpha 1 (α_1) lies ten times as far, at 1000 light years.

Both distances seem close compared to the 40,000-light-year distance to the faint globular cluster M30, with its myriad stars. When you view the dim glow of this globular in Capricorn through a telescope or in a standard photograph, it will appear as a dim eighth-magnitude star. M30 is 75 light years across and approaching us at a speed of some 100 miles *per second* (160 kilometers per second). Seen through optical aids, this ball-shaped cluster is typical of globulars. It has a bright, fuzzy central core with faint individual stars surrounding it. Telescopes can reveal some of its magic and transport you to another world. (See back cover.)

To frame the faint constellation area of Capricorn, you can easily draw help from outside the borders of your Starframe: Just above (north) and to the right beyond the 30 degree high window of your Stellaphane lies the very bright first magnitude star Altair, Alpha (α) Aquilae and its slightly fainter companion Beta (β) in Aquila just 2 degrees to the north. The arrow in the top right hand corner of your Stellaphane points to this landmark pair of stars in the constellation of the eagle.

FAINT CONSTELLATION — ALIGN WITH ALGEDI AND DENEB ALGEDI

CAPRICORN

(DELTA)
DENEB ALGEDI

(ALPHA)
ALGEDI

STANDARD 50 MM LENS

AIM AT ⊕ TARGET

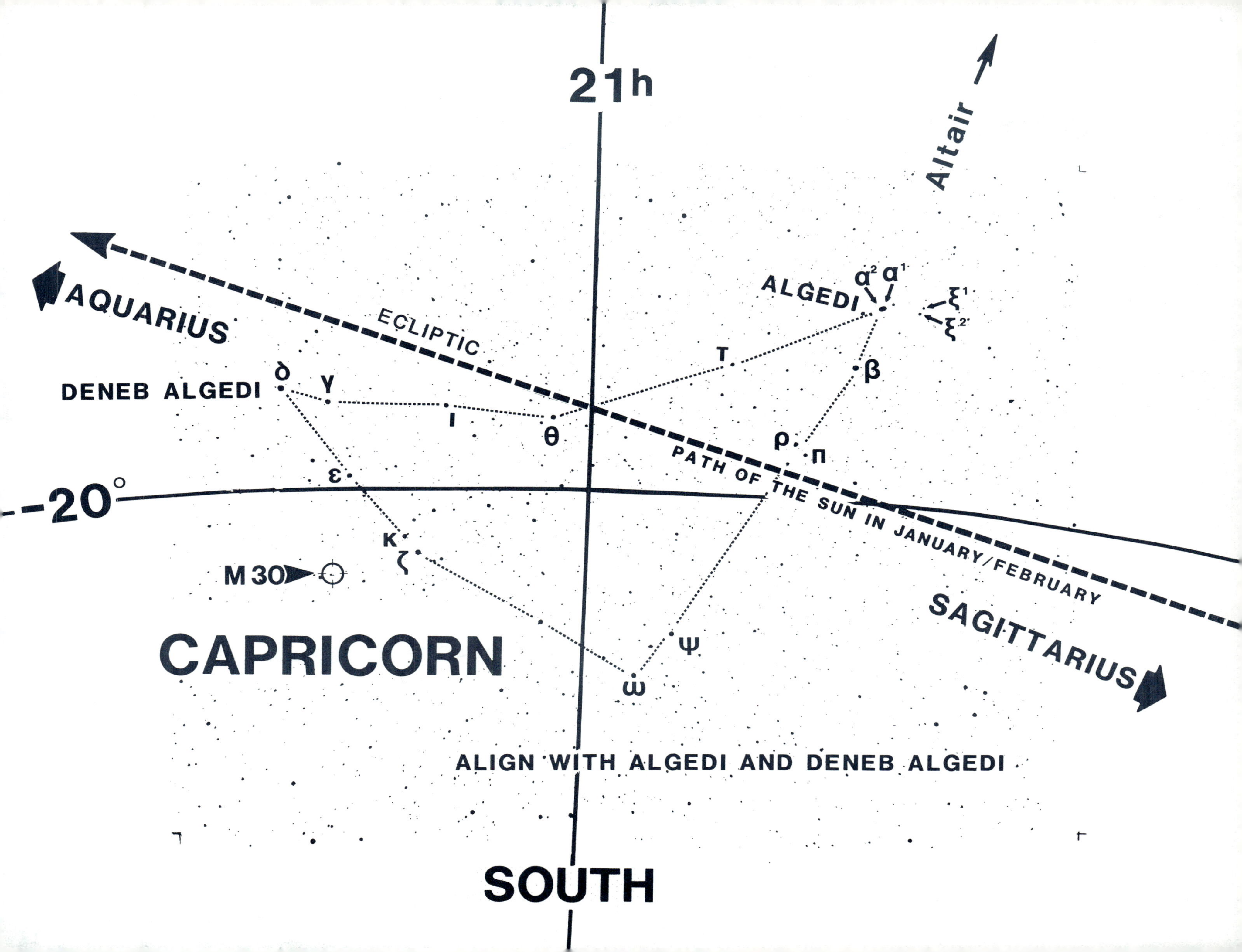

21h
Altair
AQUARIUS
ECLIPTIC
ALGEDI
α² α¹
ξ¹
ξ²
τ
β
δ
γ
DENEB ALGEDI
ι
θ
ρ
π
PATH OF THE SUN IN JANUARY/FEBRUARY
ε
20°
κ
ζ
M 30
SAGITTARIUS
ψ
CAPRICORN
ω
ALIGN WITH ALGEDI AND DENEB ALGEDI
SOUTH

Steblicom/Problicom/Viblicom

There never was a simpler way to learn than by first-hand experience. This can be called *the empirical method.* When you do anything yourself for the very first time, chances are that you will never forget it. That is why you will want to enjoy your very first "Eureka" discovery experience here and now. Let us find the jumping rabbit in the pair of illustrations on pages 93 and 95. Even though you may have already spotted it by carefully scrutinizing illustrations 20 and 21, treat yourself to your first "blinking discovery." You will see how elegant and simple it is. Just follow the easy instructions near the drawings.

For realism, we have reversed the images so that the scene appears in white on a black background. This is reminiscent of a night photograph, where tiny white stars may be discovered using the identical method. I have even introduced an extra surprise, which you can find by careful blinking scrutiny. It represents the serendipitous discovery, which is made when one finds things that one has not really been looking for. Don't forget we are looking for the jumping rabbit; anything else is a discovery bonus. Serendipity is an important part of astronomical programs.

When Clyde Tombaugh discovered the planet Pluto with a blinking device, it was not as simple as flipping pages in a book. Pairs of photographic prints copied from slides could be used in similar fashion, but in 1930 Tombaugh used a *blink microscope comparator.* (See photograph on page 86.) Such equipment is very costly, but was available to the Lowell Observatory where the twenty-four-year-old Clyde was apprenticed.

Steblicom:
For our purposes, a much less complex system is all that we need. To work in the range of the magnitudes our cameras can record, a *STEBLICOM* is quite enough. The *STE*reo *BLI*nk *COM*parator is far and away the simplest and least costly of the devices

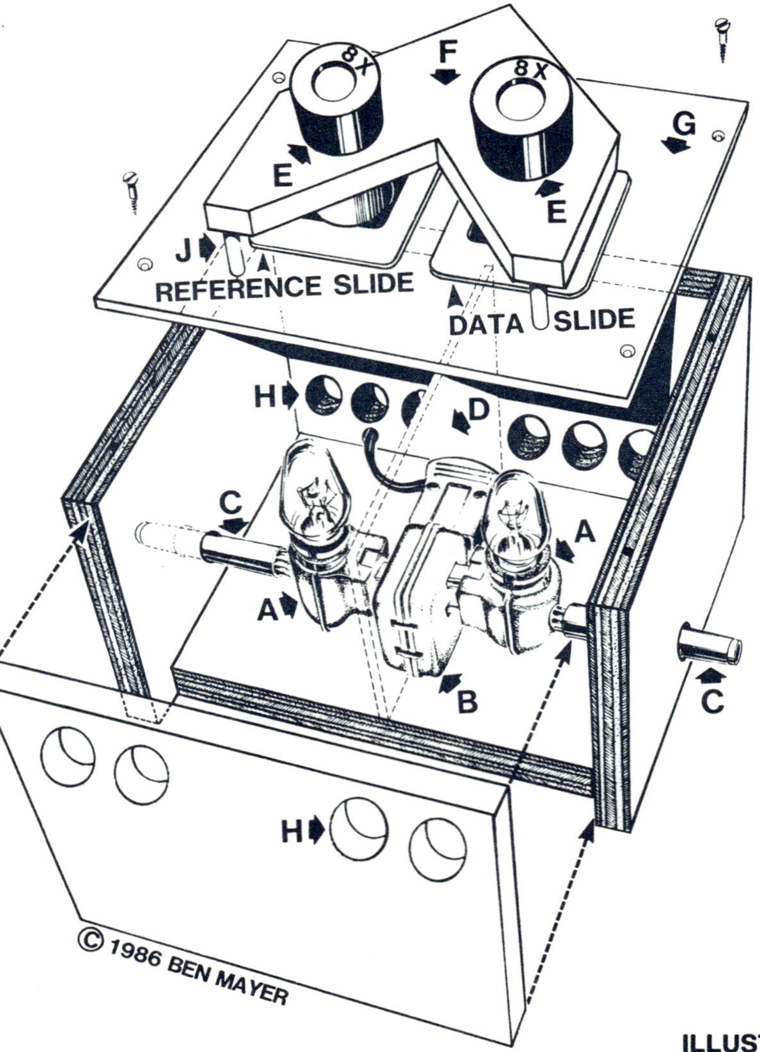

ILLUSTRATION 23

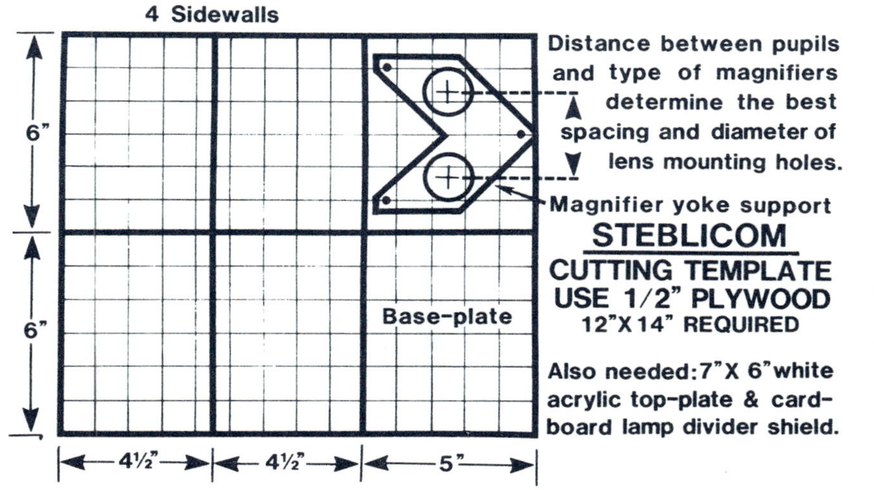

ILLUSTRATION 20A

shown here. It merely employs two small switchable night lights of 7 watts each, and two identical magnifiers of approximately 8× power. The introduction of motorized or solid-state electrical contacts into the circuits of the lamps to alternately switch them on and off allows additional opportunities for upgrading the Steblicom.

Because of its simplicity, this blinking device can also be referred to as a *discovery box* (see illustration 23). Use only Underwriters Laboratories–approved components for safety. For dramatic effect, the photographic slides to be compared may be called by their scientific names. The "before" picture is called the *reference image* and the "after" photograph the *data image.*

The underlying principle, as the name *stereo blink comparator*

The blinking principle: To obtain the "blinking effect," flip this corner landscape quickly back and forth over the one below (illustration 21A on page 95). Find the jumping rabbit and a surprise discovery object easily.

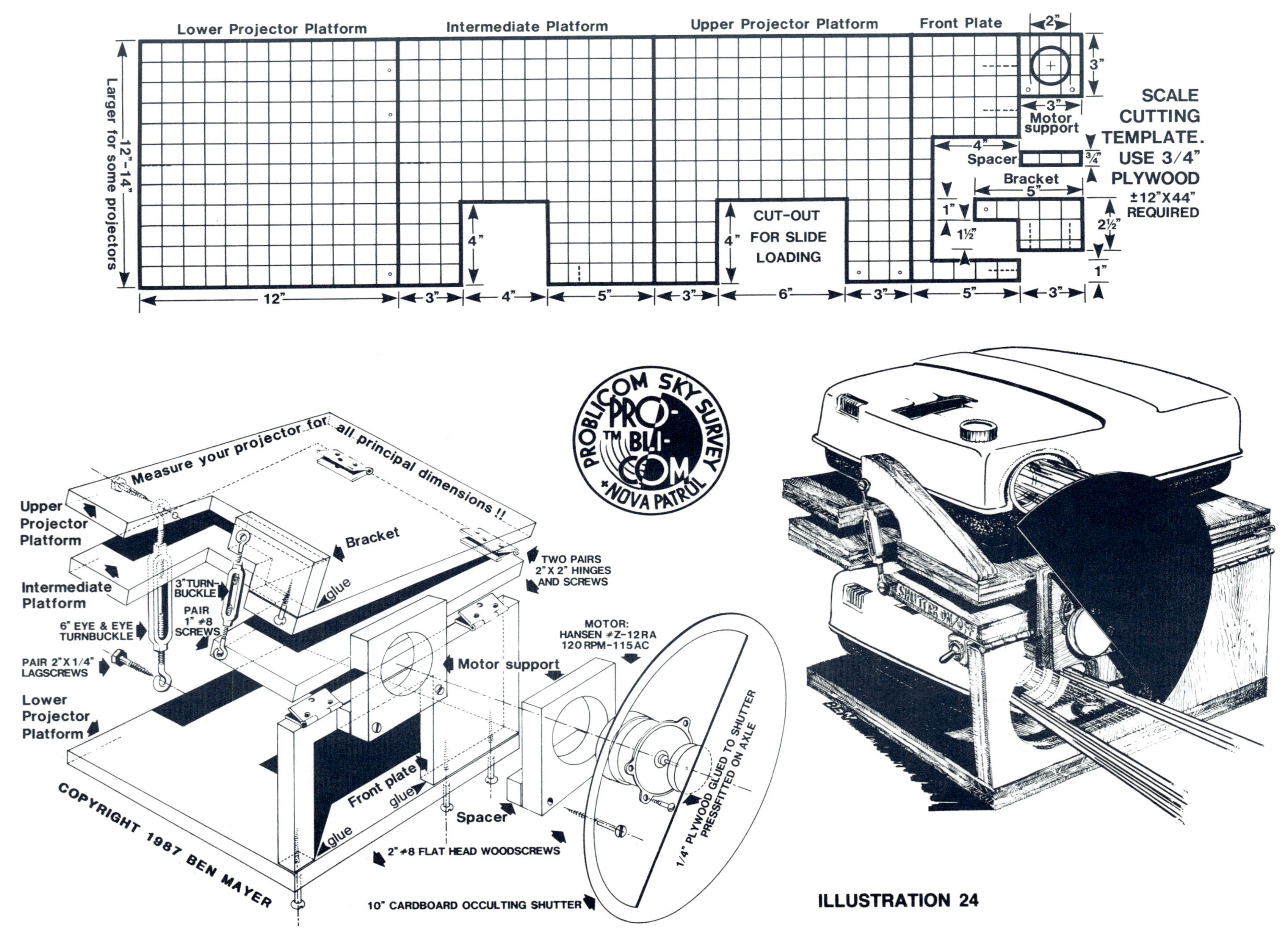

ILLUSTRATION 24

implies, is the visual aligning of two photographs of identical celestial areas taken on different dates. The two images are brought into stereo-visual accord. Then, when you turn both lights on and off alternately, or even switch on and off only one of the lighted lamps, a discovery can be made through comparison. Any object that has appeared, disappeared, moved, or changed in magnitude in the data slide will immediately draw attention to itself by "blinking." Our rabbit will silently demonstrate this simple concept.

Problicom:
The *PRO*jection *BLI*nk *COM*parator, with which popular comparison blinking was begun, had its beginnings in my desire to create a blinking system that would permit the sharing of the "Eureka" discovery experience with many others. It gave birth to the Problicom Sky Survey and Nova Patrols. Underlying the entire concept was a method that would inexpensively duplicate the costly blink comparators that are part of every astronomical observatory. The invention demanded simple components that would be available to all. Friends could pool similar slide projectors to stack on top of each other; adjustments would be made with turnbuckles available in any hardware store (see illustration 24). The Problicom was conceived to bring the stars and discovery indoors. Even on cloudy or rainy nights and weekends, the never-ending quest could continue.

The Problicom pictured here was first featured in the book *Starwatch* by this author (see the note on page 37). The device has its own trademark. The half-moon-shaped occulting shutter forming the operative blinking device is at the heart of the design and the system. By following the scale cutting template, almost anyone can construct such a discovery machine. It uses two Kodak Carousel–type projectors. Only the one on the upper platform needs a slide tray. The lower projector is manually loaded and slides are inserted individually. The preferred method is that reference slides are loaded below, with data slides inserted in the upper projector in the round slide tray. Examining several pictures in a row permits careful scrutiny and the ruling out of dust specks or misleading "stars" caused by lens reflections. In photography, it is not uncommon for bright stars or planets, even if outside the direct field of photographic view, to cause such spurious spots, which can be highly confusing.

A "high-gain" projection screen completes the required equipment. Whitewashed walls or bedsheets have been used successfully as projecting surfaces. When Problicoms are used in schools, large classes can share blinking sessions. With long-focus projection lenses, very large audiences can be addressed. (A slight modification in the placement of the occulting shutter will be required.) It may be necessary to adapt the wooden double platform to the specific dimensions of different projector models.

How blinking works: For a simple demonstration of how all blinking devices work, rapidly flip the preceding landscape (illustration 20A on page 93) back and forth over the one shown here. You will find the rabbit. Can you find "object X"?

ILLUSTRATION 21A

Viblicom:
It is only fitting that the latest and most sophisticated of the various blinking devices should be the last one shown (see illustration 25). Blink comparison has long been the exclusive province of professional astronomers with access to equipment today costing in excess of one hundred fifty thousand dollars. Extraordinary computer systems that can be used for blinking have not changed matters; searches and patrols for discovery have been denied to all except a select few.

The recent invention (U.S. Patent 4,404,590) of the *VIBLICOM* (*VI*-deo *BLI*nk *COM*parator) brings a new method to science for a fraction of the cost of earlier systems. It combines the worldwide-standard 35mm film format with state-of-the-art video imaging, enhancing, measuring, storage, and retrieval. Here the underlying principle is a simple so-called beam splitter, as suggested by the logotype shown in illustration 25.

ILLUSTRATION 25

Mystery Object X:
We should not forget to ask whether you have discovered anything else beside the blinking rabbit in illustrations 20A and 21A. At the risk of divulging the secret, "object X" is in the data image 21A. It will only show up when compared to the companion picture, or reference image, 20A. Thus, it convincingly represents what can happen while you use blinking photographs to help find bright moving planets in the Zodiac, i.e., the rabbit. Mystery object X, however faint, can be a true discovery—a significant find.

As mentioned on page 70, this could have happened to me with any of the photographs I took in August 1975, while actually shooting for shooting stars. Instead of meteors, my camera recorded Nova Cygni 1975. But I cannot claim the *discovery* of this cataclysmic event. At the time, I had no blinking device; I did not even know that comparison blinking existed. Today, a discovery box or machine will put anyone on the path to serious astronomical discovery.

There are 41,253 square degrees of sky in the celestial sphere. The heavens, quite literally, are the last unexplored frontier. Only now, today, in the twentieth century, can simple photography and comparison blinking be combined to yield important celestial discoveries.

P.S. The mystery object X is a rare bird (threatened with extinction) that has settled on the lowest branch of the extreme left tree. In your first pairs of photographs your own discovery object X may be a comet, which will bear your name into the remotest future.

Project Aquarius

Here is the central watersign. Its very name bespeaks *aqua,* the liquid element. It has long been described as the symbol of the water carrier, an imaginary man or boy carrying water in a jar. Just like Virgo, this constellation is very spread out. It too needed the wide-angle 35mm lens to fit all of its stars into our starcharts. That is why we must hold our Starframe 11–15 inches from the eye again when we try to observe this pictogram.

Hold your Stellaphane Starframe as shown above the southern horizon. It is not difficult to correct for the more widely spaced stars of the Aquarius constellation by holding your Starframe at the wide-angle 11–15-inch distance instead of the standard 15–18 inches. If you want to photograph the entire starfield to match the starchart shown in illustration 26, you may want to splurge on a fast (used?) 35 or 40mm focal length lens for your SLR camera, to interchange with the standard 50mm focal length when possible. Besides Virgo and Aquarius, there is only one other such wide starfield. It is the following constellation of Pisces.

But not to worry, because you can shoot the main Aquarius area with a standard 50mm lens. It is easy to anticipate what your film will record: Simply hold a plain Starframe (without Stellaphane overlay) at the regular 15–18-inch distance from the eye. Under dark skies, this frame will outline the kite-shaped head of the pictogram only. Simply aim your basic Starframe or camera half a dimension higher (north) and very slightly further right (west). Helpfully, it is in this area of the constellation that the two brightest anchor stars of the kite are found. Alpha (**α**) Aquarii, magnitude 3.0, and Beta (**β**) Aquarii, magnitude 2.9, should be visible even in moderate light pollution.

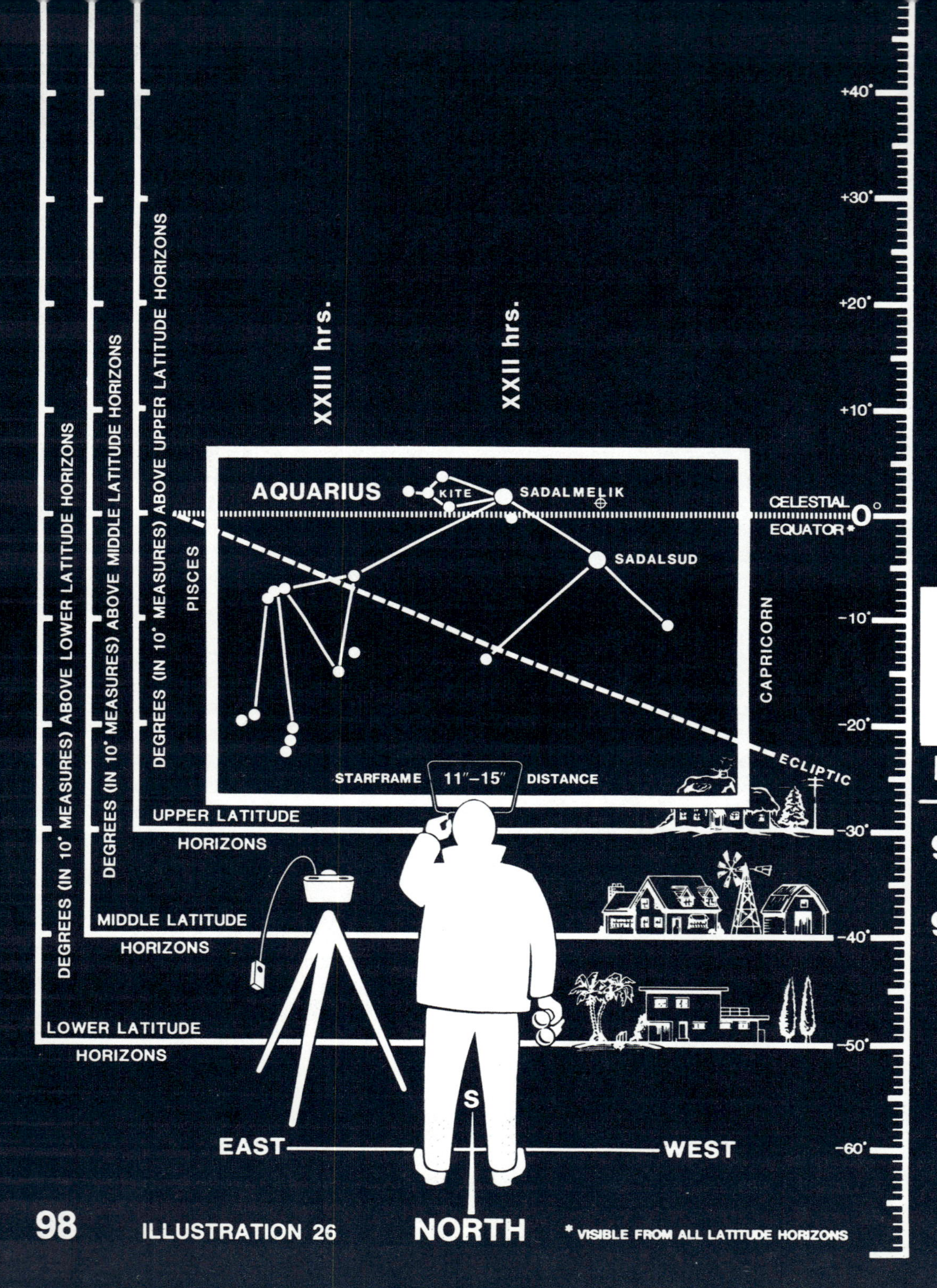

ILLUSTRATION 26

CULMINATIONS OF THE AQUARIUS STARFIELD
(see illustration on left)

Hold the Starframe only 11–15 inches from the eye

*June 15-July 1	at 5:00 am	= 05:00 hours
*July 1-July 15	at 4:00 am	= 04:00 hours
*July 15-August 1	at 3:00 am	= 03:00 hours
*August 1-August 15	at 2:00 am	= 02:00 hours
*August 15-September 1	at 1:00 am	= 01:00 hours
*September 1-September 15	at MIDNIGHT	= 24:00 hours
*September 15-October 1	at 11:00 pm	= 23:00 hours
*October 1-October 15	at 10:00 pm	= 22:00 hours
October 15-November 1	at 8:00 pm	= 20:00 hours
November 1-November 15	at 7:00 pm	= 19:00 hours

*Times on these dates are adjusted for daylight saving time.

AQUARIUS

L.Y.	BRIGHTEST STARS		MAG.
950	α ALPHA	SADALMELIK LUCKSTAR OF THE KING (AR)	3.0
980	β BETA	SADALSUD LUCKIEST OF LUCKSTARS (AR)	2.9
95	γ GAMMA	SADALACHBIA LUCKSTAR OF TENTS (AR)	3.8
98	δ DELTA	SKAT SHIN OF WATERBEARER (AR)	3.3
170	ε EPSILON	AL BALI SWALLOWER'S LUCKSTAR (AR)	3.7
75	ζ ZETA	ZETA AQR	3.6

For the ancient Arabs, the stars in this region held an association with luck and good fortune. The Alpha star is called Sadalmelik, meaning "the luckstar of the king." The Beta star is Sadalsud, which translates as "the luckiest of luckstars." By connecting Alpha (α) and Beta (β), we form the upper section of the tail of the little kite. The westernmost Epsilon (ε) star at the tail end is called Al Bali, which translates as "the swallower's luckstar." The southernmost star of the kite, as it glides on its side, is the third-magnitude Gamma (γ) star Sadalachbia, denoted "the luckstar of the tents" for nomadic desert tribes.

The unfailing reliability of the positions of the stars may make you try your camera once more, to collect the starlight of this important starfield. Set elevations at different angles above the southern horizon again, trying 35 degrees, 40 degrees, and 45 degrees. In this manner, one of the pictures will show the kite perfectly from your latitude at the correct culmination times listed.

M2 is a globular cluster within reach of binoculars from a dark observing site, but is really a telescopic object. Otherwise it may look—as it did to Charles Messier in September 1760—like "a nebulosity without stars." (See back cover.)

Another object that may catch your eye through a good pair of binoculars under excellent seeing conditions is the large "sunflower nebula," also known as the "double helix." In the NGC *(New General Catalogue)* it is listed under the number NGC 7293. It is extremely faint but very large, with a diameter about half that of the moon. Because of its low brightness, you might only observe a large, circular, hazy patch.

The third magnitude star Zeta (ζ) Aquarii is a double, a pair of two identical stars of magnitude 4.5 each. You may want to test a telescope at a starparty (see "A First Telescope," pages 102–104) to check its optical ability by trying to "separate" this double star in the center of the kite into its components. If you swing the 'scope a little to the right (west) you will be able to find Messier's M2 (see above) at the same elevation. This technique is called *starhopping.*

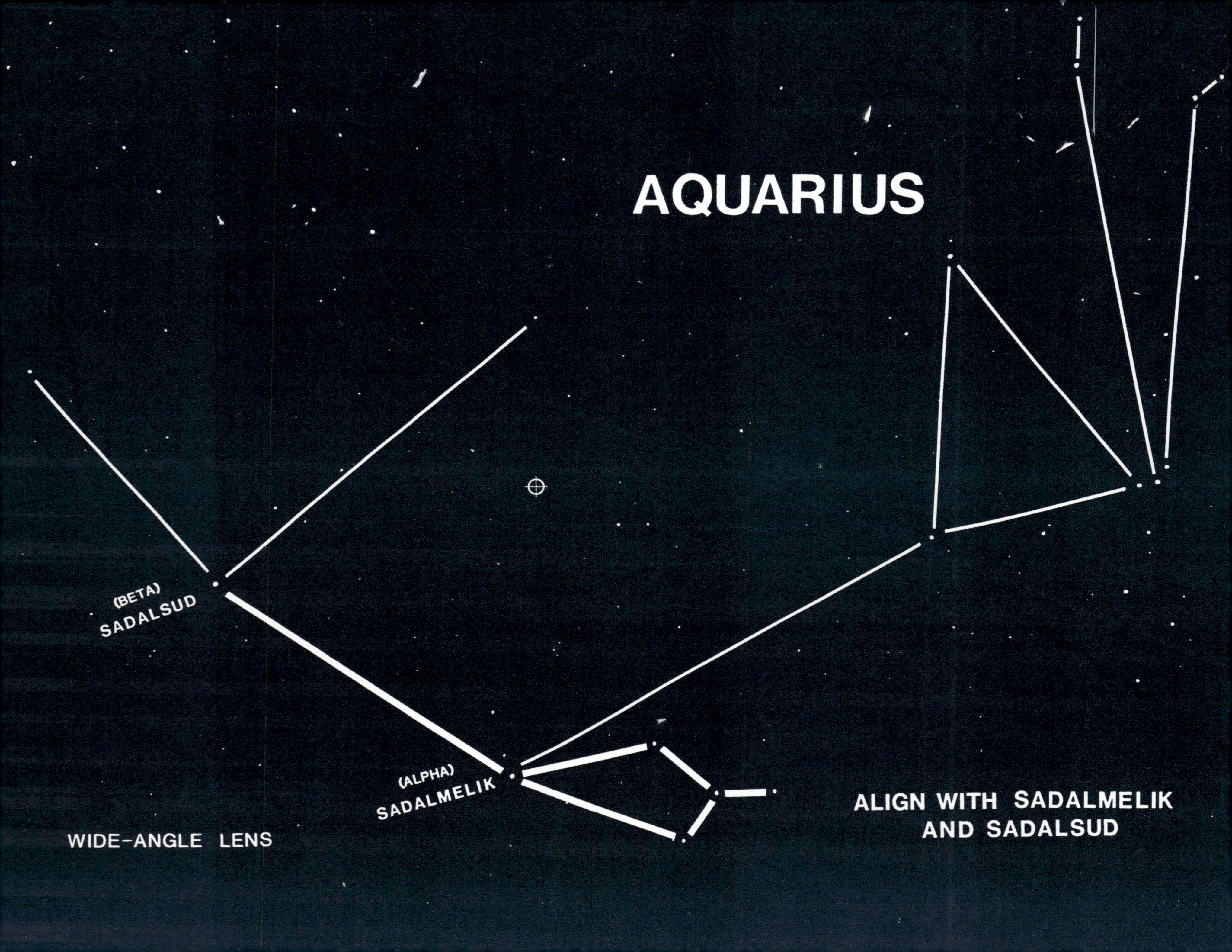

AQUARIUS

(BETA)
SADALSUD

(ALPHA)
SADALMELIK

WIDE-ANGLE LENS

ALIGN WITH SADALMELIK
AND SADALSUD

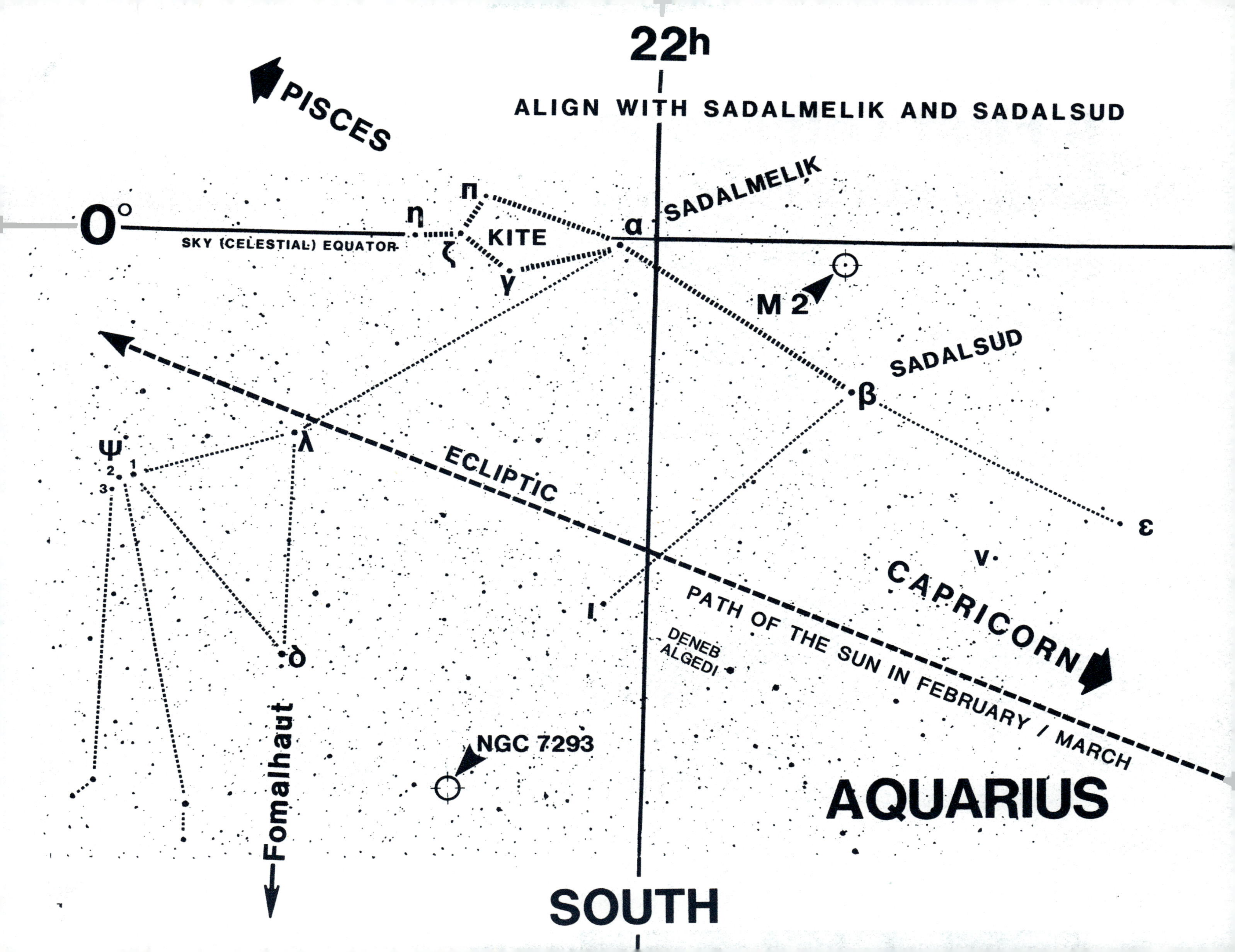
22h
ALIGN WITH SADALMELIK AND SADALSUD
PISCES
SADALMELIK
0°
SKY (CELESTIAL) EQUATOR
KITE
M 2
SADALSUD
ECLIPTIC
CAPRICORN
PATH OF THE SUN IN FEBRUARY / MARCH
DENEB ALGEDI
NGC 7293
Fomalhaut
AQUARIUS
SOUTH

A First Telescope

There are many kinds of telescopes, and magazines advertise their features and merits (see "Resources," page 135). Instead of following conventional optical descriptions, this chapter begins by discussing the importance of the strength and stability of telescope *mounts, tripods,* or *supports.* Rather than repeatedly sighting-in your system on the Pole star (see page 78), you may want to install a rigid, strong, permanently aligned pier close to your home. Then all you need do is attach any camera or telescopic system to such a mechanical stand and you are ready to observe or photograph at any time.

We have already presented the least expensive drive to "*S*top *T*he *E*arth, *L*ock *A*ll *S*tars" (you may want to screw your *STELAS* through the tee nut (Item E) to such a setup (see page 77). Please don't forget that your standard 35mm-format camera and its conventional basic 50mm lens can get you deeply involved in astronomy and deeper into space than many highly touted telescopes. If you want to obtain firsthand practical information on telescopes or related products, a phone call can get you started:

Contact a nearby high school principal and then inquire of an earth science teacher where and when local amateur astronomers meet. If there is a college with an astronomy department near you, it can surely assist. Perhaps you can call a local observatory. Amateur astronomy clubs have meetings year-round, where telescopes are discussed and even shown. But it will be during favorable weather that "star parties" are held, usually in dark locations on new moon weekends (see "The Moon," pages 54–56). There you will be able to meet telescope fanciers from all walks of life.

Starlovers come in various sizes and shapes just like telescopes. You will meet and see a wide selection. Some have home-built systems constructed with love and elbow grease on tight budgets, while others may boast store-bought ready-to-go products, for which money may have been no object.

Join an amateur club—memberships are mostly very reasonable. Look into and through as many telescopes as you can. Don't forget to check the stability of their tripods or supports. Do the stars tremble or dance while you observe or after you refocus the eyepiece? How long does it take for the vibration to stop or "damp out"? Telescope owners will gladly show off their pride and joys. Ask to see a globular cluster after making sure in these pages that it will be in the sky at the time. Request a Messier object in the Zodiac and note how quickly—or slowly—a telescope responds to its owner's bidding. Get to look at the same object through several different 'scopes to compare the clarity or crispness of what you observe.

As a rule of thumb, the long and slender telescopes that look like the spyglasses of old are so-called *refractors,* in which lenses alone do the magnifying (the larger the objective lens, the more costly the instrument). The shorter, squat telescopes are the more popular *reflectors,* in which a round mirror gathers the light for magnification (the larger the mirror, and thus the diameter of the barrel, the more desirable the system). Inquire about an instrument's problems, if any. Don't be afraid to ask for and note the aperture and the f-ratio (speed) of comparative makes. When you find what you want, you may even wish to check in the classified section of publications (see "Resources," page 135) to consider a used telescope. Unless it has been deliberately abused, little can really go wrong with such an instrument. Many a secondhand optical system is a recent "orphan" whose former owner may have lost interest in it, never realizing its hidden talents or driving powers. You can ignore cosmetic blemishes as long as the optics are fine. Under the night sky, all telescopes appear black.

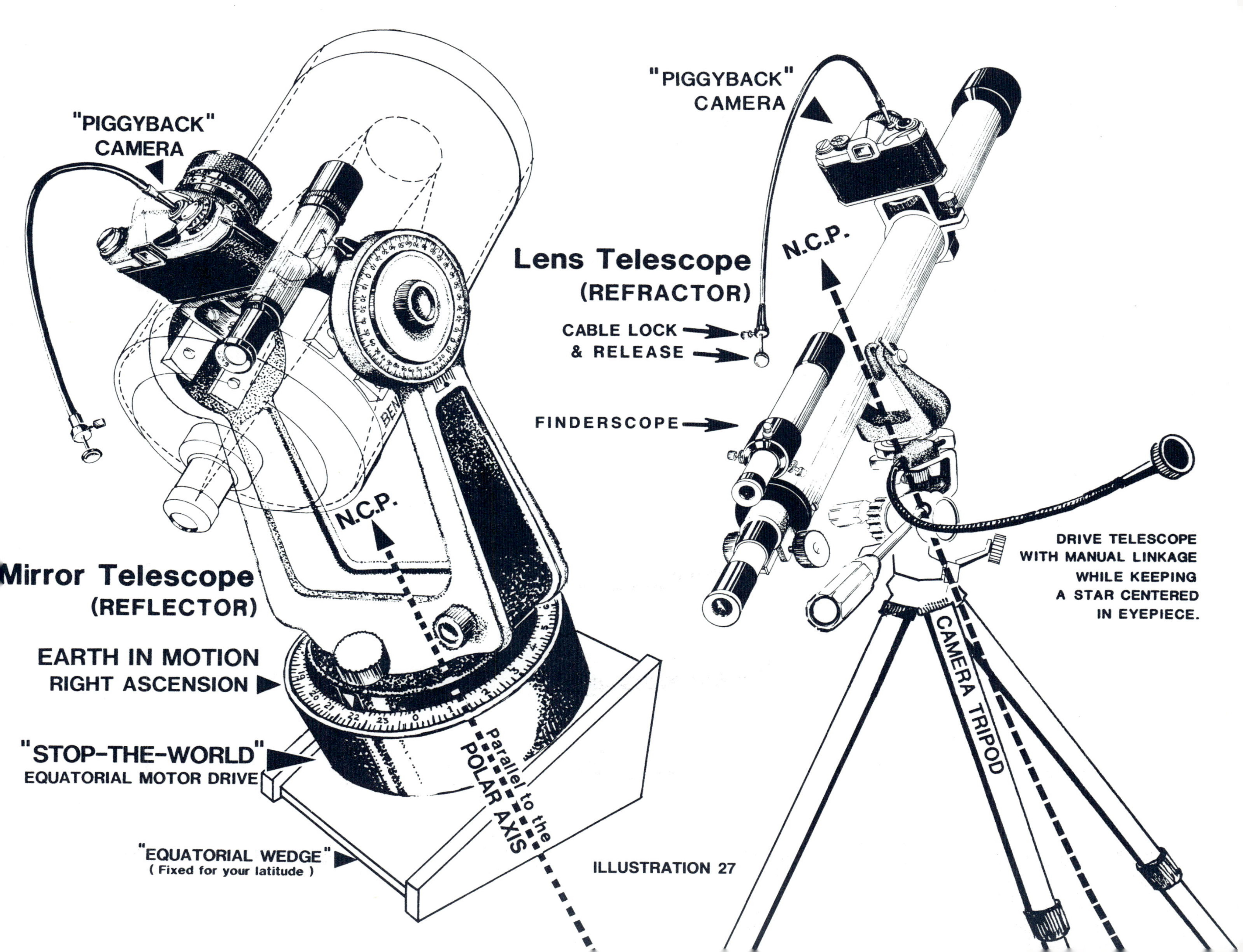

ILLUSTRATION 27

Be sure you obtain a manual with a used telescope and read all instructions on how to "polar align" the instrument. The importance of a motorized drive system cannot be overemphasized, for both observation and photography (see "Stop the World," pages 76–78). Such drives are always available with electrical adaptors so they can be connected to car batteries in the field. Alignment with the North Star is central to telescopes everywhere. Check into the so-called Dobsonian telescopes with their large mirrors. These are systems that you may be able to build for yourself.

It is extremely important to point out that *all* major astronomical images you have ever seen, whether nebulae, galaxies, or comets, were photographs—without exception. Most were long time exposures, some with the duration of minutes, others of hours. Many such photographs were taken by professionals with optical giants like the Palomar Mountain telescope. These permit high magnifications because of the size of their mirrors or objectives, and their light-grasping capabilities.

Do not be fooled by the words *power* and *magnification.* A telescope must be able to gather the light of celestial objects, must have the ability to "resolve" faint stars by means of a very large aperture diameter. Even the best optics cannot magnify what they are unable to "see." All you will finally need for a telescope is a bracket or screw to attach your SLR *on top of it* (see illustration 27). Such a piggyback arrangement allows you to view the sky telescopically and then take a record (or reference) photograph of just where you have been. The piggyback attachment is sometimes called a *coaxial* camera mount (meaning "on the same axis").

All telescopes come equipped with viewfinders in the form of so-called *finder 'scopes.* A finder 'scope is a minitelescope that should be aligned during daylight hours parallel to the main 'scope so that a distant object—or the moon—is centered in both instruments. Three or six little screws are provided to align, or *collimate,* the finder 'scope.

Motor-driven systems should be provided with an *equatorial wedge,* or pier, which will facilitate lining up the telescope on the North Pole. These wedges or supports differ from one 'scope to another and will be described in the instruction manual. They relate to your site's latitude on our planet.

Most telescopes will accept one or more eyepieces, which have their focal length engraved on them. Always begin viewing through the lowest-power ocular (largest focal length). Even this may send you reeling when you train your system on the moon. Note that north and south are now reversed (in the finder 'scope, too), which demonstrates their difference in relation to binoculars (see page 62).

A common problem besetting telescope users is the dew that can settle on cool glass surfaces during nights when the humidity is high. A portable hair dryer will readily remove such moisture. Condensation may make it difficult or impossible to look through telescopes at such times. The body of a camera can be wrapped in a polyethylene bag, with just the lens peeking out to be blow-dried at intervals.

Today, even a modest first telescope will give you powers equaling the reach of professional astronomers during the flowering of astronomy at the famous Royal Observatory in Greenwich. Can you imagine a twentieth-century store-bought refractor in the hands of Galileo in 17th century Rome? Just try to picture a modern reflector telescope being presented to Hipparchus the Greek.

Project Pisces

Pisces, the starfield of the Fishes, is the third "wide-angle" constellation. It is also the last of what the ancients called the watersigns. The pictogram stars, even Alrischa, Alpha (α) Piscium, are fainter than third magnitude, and that is why we will be best guided by the "rectangle" of the neighboring constellation of Pegasus and the two bright second-magnitude stars in its left side. When you hold your Starframe 45 degrees above the southern horizon at the closer range of 11–15 inches from your eye, you should be on target.

The two brightest stars in your Starframe due south at culmination are therefore not Piscian stars, but belong to the celestial horse of Pegasus. The Pegasus square should really be called "the rectangle of Pegasus"). It is cradled between the two arms of the large *L* shape of Pisces. Check to make sure that there are no planets swimming among the fishes. In "wide-angle" regions, the chances are greater that such bright, misleading "stars" are somewhere in or near your field of view.

Your Pisces anchor star is Algenib, the Gamma (γ) star in Pegasus, which should be a little to the right of center in your Starframe when held 11–15 inches from your face. This bottom-left-corner star of the dominant box in Pegasus will quickly reveal the rest of the second-magnitude stars of the bright, unmistakable "square of Pegasus." Its four stars should fit squarely into the upper right-hand corner of your Stellaphane Starframe.

Once you have located this easy-to-spot four-cornered shape and have aligned your Stellaphane Starframe with it, the rest of the pictogram takes shape. You can find the star Alrischa, meaning "the knot," connecting the imaginary ropes tying together the two fishes. Alrischa, Alpha (α) Piscium, at magnitude 3.9, is not the

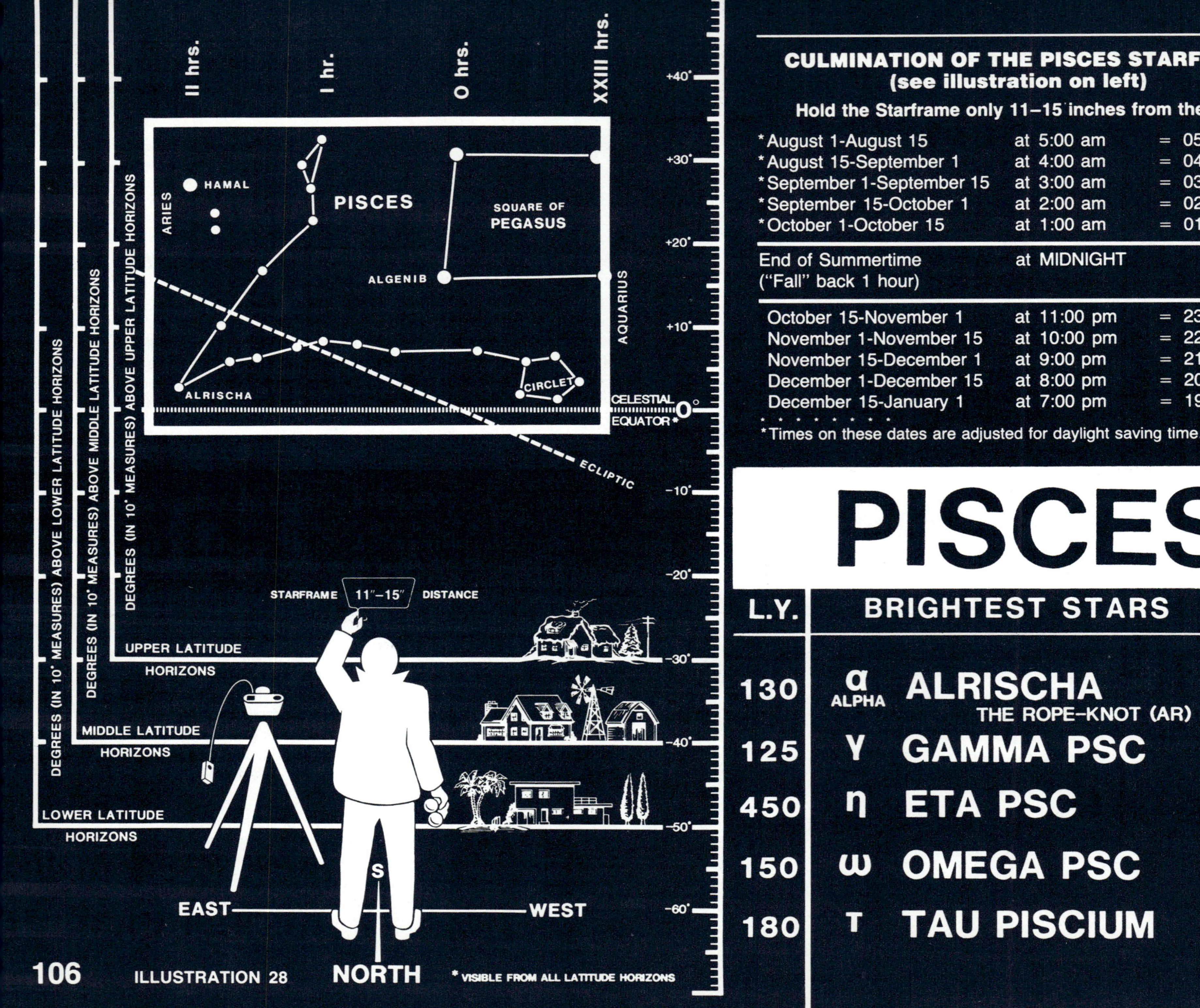

ILLUSTRATION 28

CULMINATION OF THE PISCES STARFIELD (see illustration on left)

Hold the Starframe only 11–15 inches from the eye

*August 1-August 15	at 5:00 am	=	05:00 hours
*August 15-September 1	at 4:00 am	=	04:00 hours
*September 1-September 15	at 3:00 am	=	03:00 hours
*September 15-October 1	at 2:00 am	=	02:00 hours
*October 1-October 15	at 1:00 am	=	01:00 hours
End of Summertime ("Fall" back 1 hour)	at MIDNIGHT		
October 15-November 1	at 11:00 pm	=	23:00 hours
November 1-November 15	at 10:00 pm	=	22:00 hours
November 15-December 1	at 9:00 pm	=	21:00 hours
December 1-December 15	at 8:00 pm	=	20:00 hours
December 15-January 1	at 7:00 pm	=	19:00 hours

*Times on these dates are adjusted for daylight saving time.

PISCES

L.Y.	BRIGHTEST STARS		MAG.
130	α ALPHA	ALRISCHA THE ROPE-KNOT (AR)	3.9
125	γ	GAMMA PSC	3.8
450	η	ETA PSC	3.7
150	ω	OMEGA PSC	4.0
180	τ	TAU PISCIUM	4.7

easiest star to see. Under dark skies, however, you cannot miss it with a properly held Starframe to guide you.

If you do not have a 35 or 40mm wide-angle lens, but instead own a SLR with a standard 50mm lens, you can still add to your collection of photographic Zodiac records (or start one). Here is what you should do: place the Pegasus anchor star Algenib in the top left corner of a plain Starframe (without Stellaphane), holding it 15–18 inches from your eye. You will now have framed the lower of the two fishes. Popularly, this little asterism is known as "the circlet." View this area through binoculars that surround the asterism entirely in their field of view. This distinctive circular grouping can thus be observed to include fainter stars than the naked eye will be able to see. They round out what was early regarded as one of the pair of fishes. The other fish, further north, is triangular in shape. (See back cover.)

A telescope may sometimes help you to find a variable star.[1] Y Piscium—not to be confused with Gamma (γ) Piscium—is also in the circlet. The variable Y Piscium changes from telescopic magnitude 9.0 to near invisibility at magnitude 12.0, and back again over a 3.7-day period. You may want to try your hand at spotting and observing this remarkable object. Then turn any telescope on Alrischa, Alpha (α) Piscium, and find that it really is a double, with components of magnitudes 4.3 and 5.3.

It is in the constellation of Pisces that the sun crosses the celestial equator at the point and at the time of the vernal equinox *in March,* to announce the arrival of spring. Then the sun leaves behind the southern celestial hemisphere and its Zodiac constellations to reenter the northern skies. This marks the zero position in R.A., from which the twenty-four hours of right ascension are numbered and counted (see "Point of Spring Equinox" on page 109). Today you may want to try Project Equinox/Solstice (see pages 30–32) again during the culmination dates of the constellation Pisces, and record your autumn findings. Because now, during September, the autumnal equinox occurs. As you can readily observe during September noons, the sun will stand at exactly the same elevation angle in the sky as it did last spring, six months ago, and will stand again next year, six and twelve moons from now. Nights and days are of equal lengths these days, as when the sun crosses through the unseen stars of Virgo in daytime in March.

• • • • • • • •

[1] Many bright variable stars have letters beginning with R, S, T, U, etc., plus the possesive constellation name.

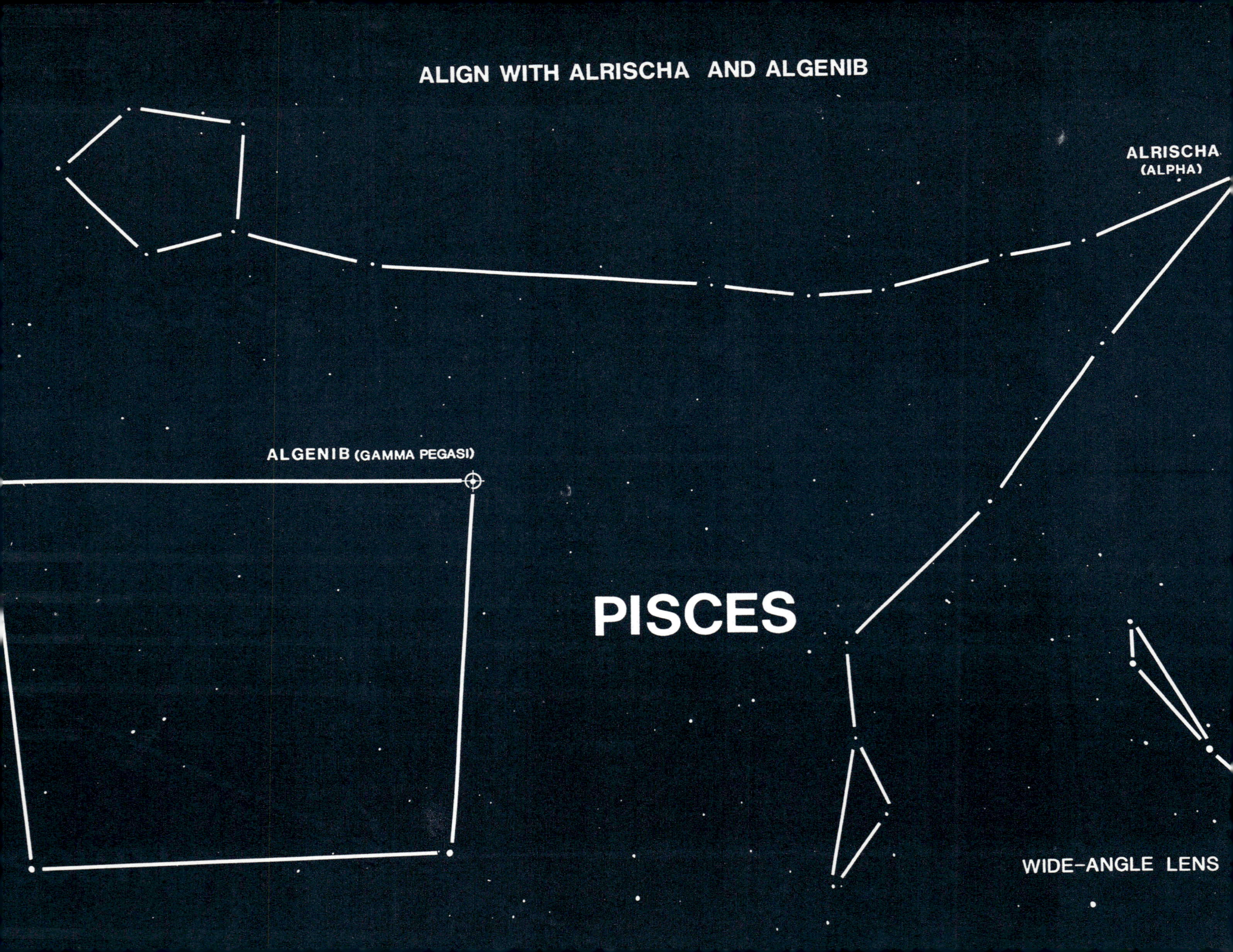

ALIGN WITH ALRISCHA AND ALGENIB

ALRISCHA
(ALPHA)

ALGENIB (GAMMA PEGASI)

PISCES

WIDE-ANGLE LENS

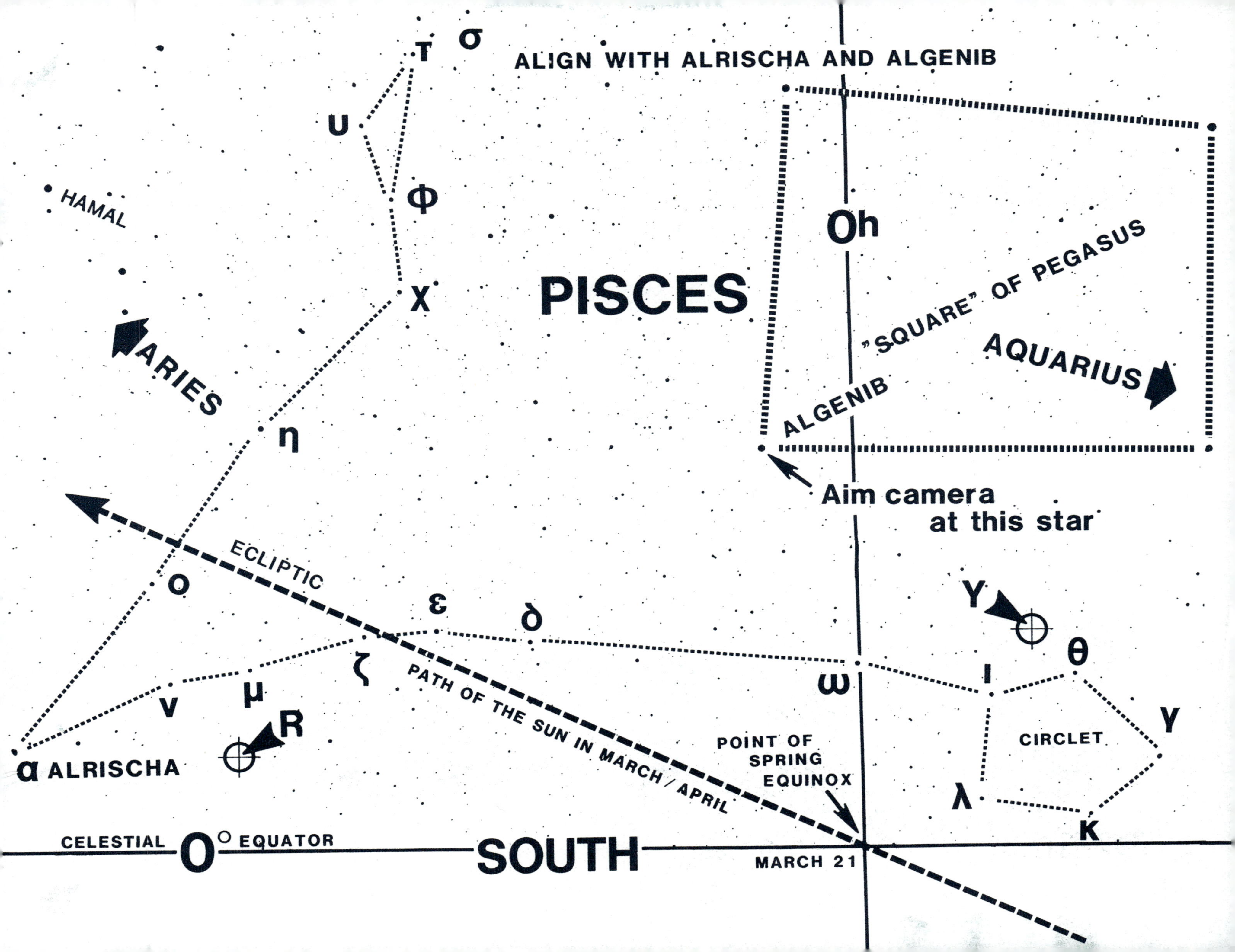
ALIGN WITH ALRISCHA AND ALGENIB
HAMAL
ARIES
PISCES
0h
"SQUARE" OF PEGASUS
AQUARIUS
ALGENIB
Aim camera at this star
ECLIPTIC
PATH OF THE SUN IN MARCH / APRIL
Y
R
α ALRISCHA
CIRCLET
POINT OF SPRING EQUINOX
CELESTIAL 0° EQUATOR
SOUTH
MARCH 21
τ
σ
υ
φ
χ
η
ο
ε
δ
ζ
ν
μ
ω
ι
θ
γ
λ
κ

Surrogate Skies

In dictionaries, a *surrogate* is defined as "something that serves as a substitute or as an alternate." It has become a key word in speech and writing. Not surprising, then, is the fact that in the domain of the stars, "surrogate skies" can also be found. But just as in any other area, the "proxy" can never quite replace the original it is meant to imitate.

So it is with the planetarium that brings surrogate starlit skies indoors to air-conditioned, domed interiors. These allow young and old alike to marvel at the constellations under near-perfect conditions. We should certainly admire the extraordinary technological magic that humankind has wrought in creating such facsimile stellar environments. At the mere touch of a button we can be transported back in time to see how the heavens looked to Babylonian priests millenia ago. Another flip of a switch can carry us a hundred thousand years into a future we may sense but will never see.

Thus it was during my first planetarium visit, as a youngster in Munich, Germany, that my father took me to see the original, the very first Zeiss planetarium projector. It wove its spell in the Deutsches Museum, half a century ago. Newer projectors today weave the same magic in planetariums worldwide. Since then, I have often sought refuge under real stars, as on the day my mother died. That melancholy November night, the dazzling light of Hamal, the brightest Alpha (α) star in Aries (pages 113–115), beckoned to me. There under solemn skies, fleeting photons caressed the retinas of my eyes. Here was subtle visual energy that had journeyed through interstellar space at the speed of light the entire seventy-five years of my mother's life: starlight on its way from times past into the unfathomable hereafter, at the incredible speed of 186,000 miles per second.

Falling twilight in the country or the mountains always evokes a deep sense of yearning for the coming stars beneath blackening velvet skies. In a planetarium I can experience parallel sensations. Here they are underlined by fitting stereo music, often classical, to help create an appropriate mood. Even shooting stars may be seen darting across the skies, a projection of surrogate meteor showers.

It may be the knowledge deep inside my consciousness and the intangible feeling in my heart that make me prefer the real sky to arc-lamp star alternatives. Perhaps I even miss the buzzing mosquitoes that gambol near during warm summer evenings. (Always take insect repellent on your star outings.) Could it be the ever-changing multicolored glory of the sunset, or is it the gentle aroma of pine trees scenting the fresh mountain air that sets my stage for the coming of night? I long for the incessant twilight chirping of crickets, or the occasional hooting of an owl. These are the inimitable sounds of nature that accompany the swift shadows of silent bats, crisscrossing barely overhead. You may even want to carry the melodious strains of Bach, Beethoven, or Shostakovich outdoors with you, to play softly on a tape deck as an alternate to the surrogate planetarium stereo experience itself. The possibilities are endless.

One thing should not be overlooked: the Stellaphane Starframe with its angular dimensions and pictogram tracings works just as well in a planetarium of any size as under natural skies. This means that you can practice using your zodiacal constellation Starframes at any time in planetarium star environments. You will want to know where the compass points are so that you can be seated with your back to the north, facing south. It is also preferable to sit as close to the north-south center line of the dome as possible, north of the projector.

You can always prepare the appropriate Stellaphane Starframes for any months of the year and take them to a planetarium show with you. Usually, the nightsky of the month is being shown. It will offer a unique chance to practice your starwatching indoors before attempting to duplicate your search under real skies.

There is another world of surrogate skies that has recently burst novalike upon the scene. It is the field of computer-generated video programs, with their vast libraries of starfields. These present the sky in many different modes, where even magnitudes of individual stars are shown, with up to two thousand sky and deep-sky objects listed. Moreover, they give planet positions and their times of rising, culmination, and setting. This is a relatively new arena, requiring compatible computers with graphics capabilities. By feeding in the coordinates of stellar information, anyone can "image" countless starfields and readily recognizable constellations with pictograms. Such programs reach far beyond the Zodiac shown in this book. When you trace constellations directly from a medium-sized video screen onto acetate or cellophane (see "Project Stellaphane," pages 24–26), the entire celestial sphere is brought to you for discovery. Be sure the scale of pictograms follows the Starframe, where 8 inches equal 30 degrees at the 15–18-inch distance. The basic method is explained in *Starwatch,* where twelve nonzodiacal constellations are featured, and also information on when and how to find them with Stellaphane Starframes.

The tracing from the video screen of correctly scaled monthly Stellaphane Starframes of culminating constellations can become routine. Evening or new-moon weekend TV programs telling about the history and lore of the stars and how to discover them can enlighten and entertain when presented by lovers of the sky. Discovery sweepstakes with lottery-sized prizes can be sponsored by makers of cameras and ever-faster films. The 41,253 square degrees in the celestial sphere can be divided into sky patrol areas, and cameras with data-backs can determine the earliest universal time when a photograph recording any new comet or nova was taken. By dividing each square degree[1] in the sky into 25 square minutes of arc, 1,031,325 observers could take part in a "eureka" tournament. Once we divide each square minute into 3600 squares of arc seconds, we come up with 920,192,400 individual areas in the celestial sphere. Future surrogate computer skies will be able to handle such numbers. Telescopes launched into deep space will provide ever newer and fainter targets to view and study and discover.

. . . .

[1] One degree equals 60 minutes of arc; each minute of arc is divided into 60 seconds of arc. For example, the diameter of the moon is about ½ degree (of arc) or 30 minutes (of arc), or 1800 arc seconds.

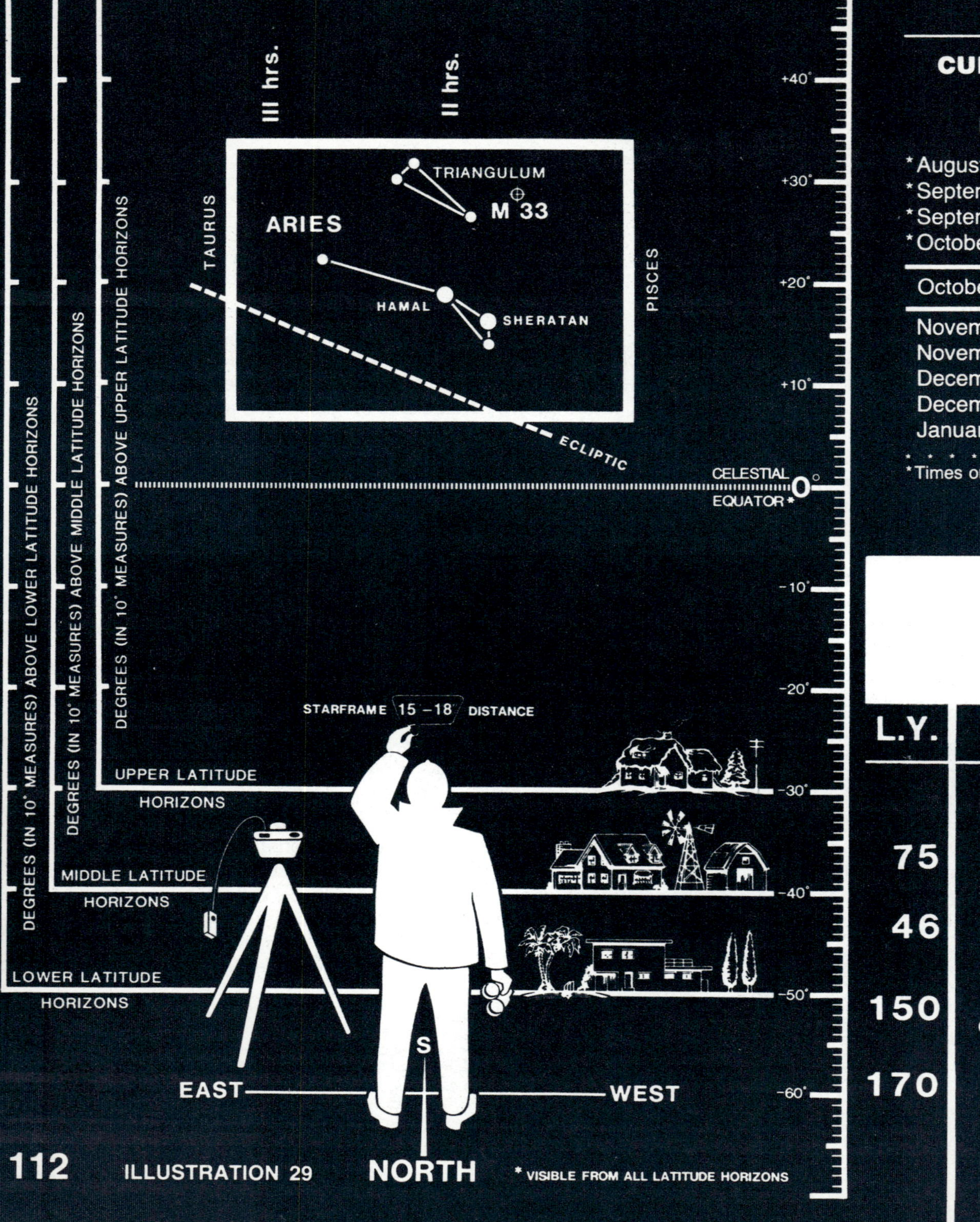

ILLUSTRATION 29

CULMINATIONS OF THE ARIES STARFIELD (see illustration on left)

Hold the Starframe 15–18 inches from the eye

*August 15-September 1	at 5:00 am	= 05:00 hours
*September 1-September 15	at 4:00 am	= 04:00 hours
*September 15-October 1	at 3:00 am	= 03:00 hours
*October 1-October 15	at 2:00 am	= 02:00 hours
October 15-November 1	at MIDNIGHT	= 24:00 hours
November 1-November 15	at 11:00 pm	= 23:00 hours
November 15-December 1	at 10:00 pm	= 22:00 hours
December 1-December 15	at 9:00 pm	= 21:00 hours
December 15-January 1	at 8:00 pm	= 20:00 hours
January 1-January 15	at 7:00 pm	= 19:00 hours

*Times on these dates are adjusted for daylight saving time.

ARIES

L.Y.	BRIGHTEST STARS	MAG.
75	α ALPHA **HAMAL** THE RAM (AR)	2.0
46	β BETA **SHERATAN** THE TWO SIGNS (AR)	2.6
150	γ GAMMA **MESARTHIM** SERVED ONES (HEBREW)	5.0
170	δ DELTA **BOTEIN** LITTLE BELLY (AR)	4.5

Project Aries

The constellation of Aries, the Ram, is yet considered by many astrologers as the first constellation of the Zodiac. We know that this honored position belongs to Pisces today, because the point of the spring equinox has moved westward by one month since astrology began to be practiced millennia ago (see page 31). You will find the Ram as shown above the southern horizon compass point.

There are only two closely spaced second-magnitude stars needed to locate Aries in the heavens. They are Hamal, Alpha (α) Arietis, at magnitude 2.0, and Sheratan, Beta (β) in Aries, at magnitude 2.6. As so often happens, the Alpha star is named after the constellation itself. *Hamal,* translated from the Arabic, means "ram." *Sheratan* stands for "the two signs" that marked the position of the equinox in the days of Hipparchus at about the time when these stars were named.

The most interesting object, by far, shown near our photographic Aries starfield is the galaxy M33, the so-called "spiral in Triangulum." Even at the distance of 2.2 million light years, it is considered a member of our "local group of galaxies." On a dark, clear night, this faint spiral galaxy is visible with binoculars when viewed from a site without any light pollution. Under near-ideal conditions, M33, this neighboring island universe, has been spotted with the naked eye by persons with excellent eyesight. The secret to such observation lies in familiarity with the region and with the surrounding stars, and also with knowing just where to look. It is of particular help to acquaint oneself with the three stars of the constellation Triangulum (the Triangle), which borders Aries on the north. As a general guide, you may want to remember to look for M33 10 degrees northwest of Hamal, Alpha (α) in Aries.

There is another technique used by astronomers when looking for stars or objects of very low magnitude or brightness. It is the method of *averted vision.* Simply stare at or scan a point 6 degrees or so to one side of the intended object. In such "corner-of-the-eye" viewing, faint light falls on the parts of your retina that are more sensitive than those that are employed in staring directly at an object. Try it sometime—the difference may amaze you. With your Stellaphane Starframe you will know exactly where to look. The 7-degree diameter of the curve of your Starframe coathanger hook will pinpoint your binocular target and help you find the exact area to observe with or without averted vision and the naked eye. Binoculars will at first offer you more luck than a telescope because of the so-called *low surface brightness* of M33, combined with its great angular size. The visual diameter has been likened to that of the moon. (See back cover.)

The spiral in Triangulum was discovered by Charles Messier on the twenty-fifth of August in the year 1764. He did not yet know the extraordinary distance that separates it from earth (see "Other Galaxies," pages 116–118).

Because Alpha (α) Arietis lies very close to us with a distance of only 75 light years separating it from earth, I sought out the star Hamal on the night when my mother died (see page 110). The dazzling light from that distant beacon had left the vicinity of the Alpha star in the constellation of the Ram at or about the time my mother had been born. This photon light energy had been journeying through interstellar space for the entire duration of my mother's life on earth, to meet my eyes on that sad night in November.

AIM CAMERA AT HAMAL
STANDARD 50 MM LENS

ARIES

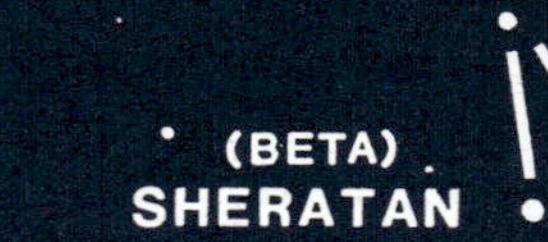

ALIGN WITH HAMAL
AND SHERATAN

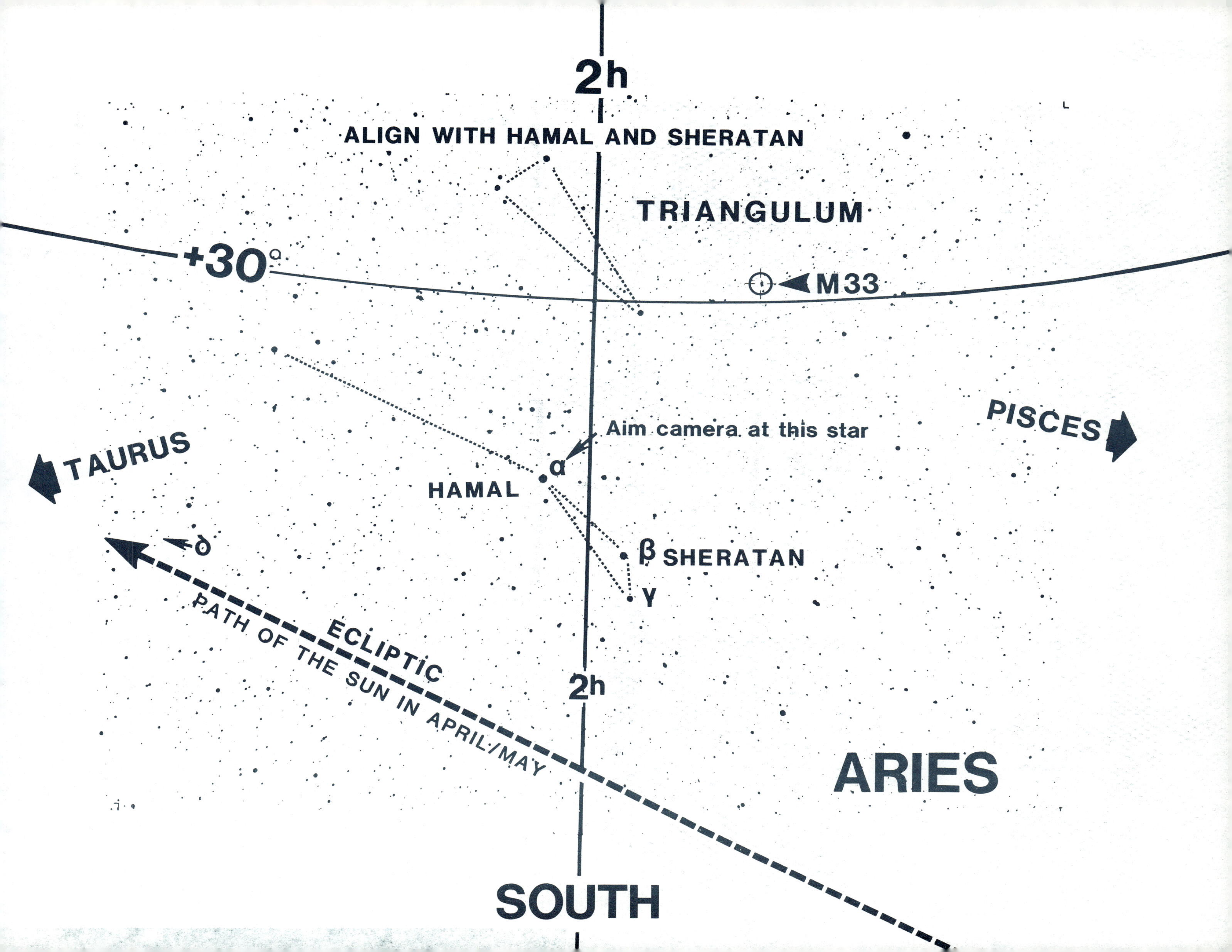
2h
ALIGN WITH HAMAL AND SHERATAN
TRIANGULUM
+30°
M33
Aim camera at this star
PISCES
TAURUS
α
HAMAL
δ
β SHERATAN
γ
ECLIPTIC
PATH OF THE SUN IN APRIL/MAY
2h
ARIES
SOUTH

Other Galaxies

Galaxies: the very word conjures up vast brilliant stellar assemblages deep in outer space. In our starcharts we have marked several of them, notably the ones within the constellations of Leo (M66, M95, and M96) and Virgo (M90 and M104) also M33 in Triangulum near Aries. Where these occur in groupings they are referred to as *clusters of galaxies*. Individually or in groups, even through optical aids, they hardly appear brilliant. Such accumulations should not be confused with galactic clusters, explained together with globulars (see page 73), many of which can be easily viewed within the saucer-shaped disc of our own home galaxy. Distances to galactic clusters, which include the famous "seven sisters," Pleiades (M45), and the Praesepe "Beehive" in Cancer (M44), as well as the bright M6 and M7 in Scorpius, are mere hundreds or thousands of light years away from us and are part of our own immediate celestial neighborhood.

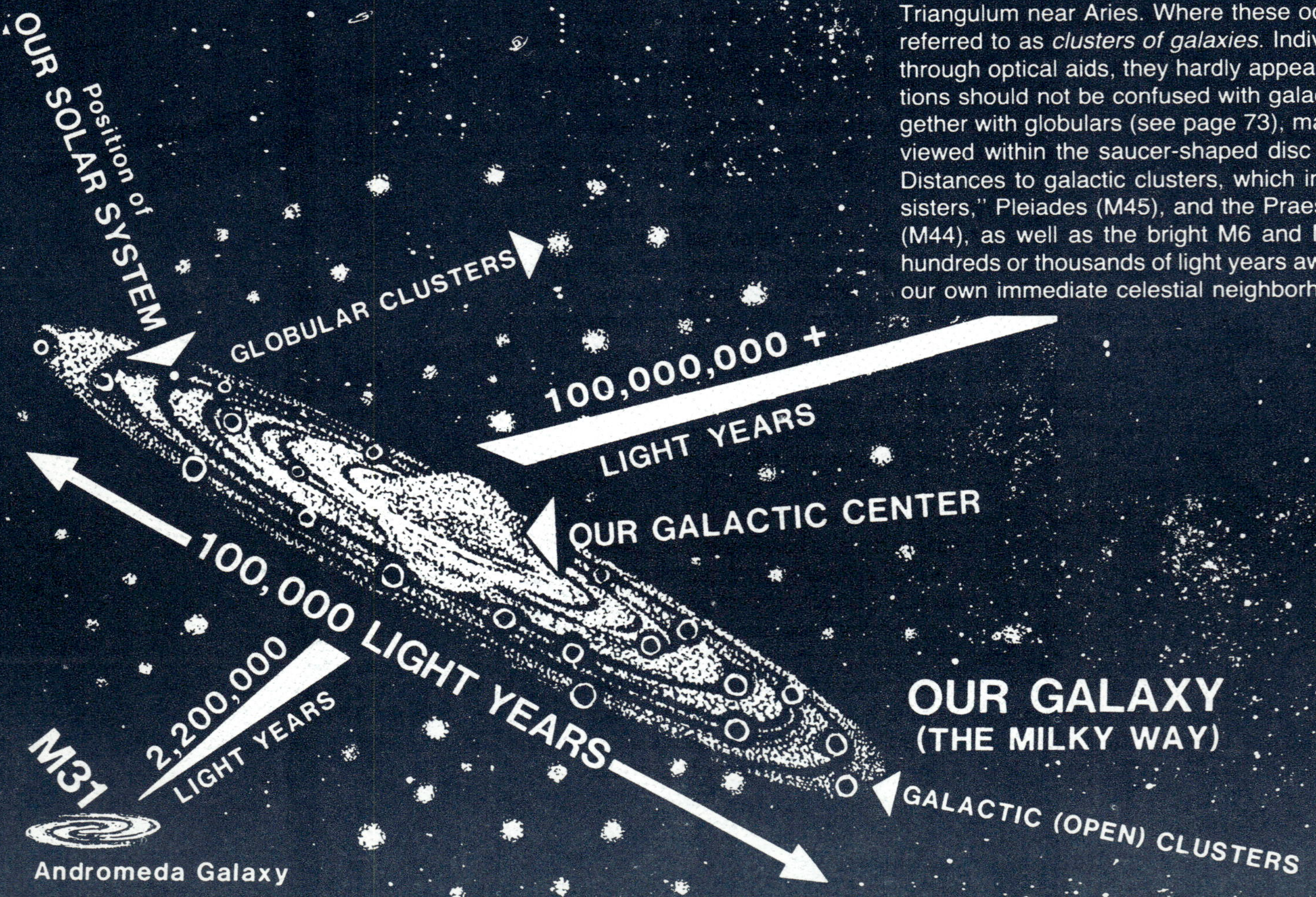

Clusters of galaxies, on the other hand, lie *millions* of light years away from earth and from our own galaxy, of which the sun, planets, and zodiacal stars form only a tiny part. Our surrounding neighborhood is called the *Milky Way galaxy*. From the inside it can only be seen "edge-on" in the form of the gossamer Milky Way, during dark summer and winter nights. This haze of light throughout history was called "the river of heaven." It was not understood until the invention of telescopes showed that what seemed to observers of old as a faint "river of light" is in reality an endless galactic conglomeration of faint and distant stars.

Each galaxy in the universe is itself such a "milky way." The galaxies are huge congregations of thousands of millions or hundreds of thousands of millions, more yet, trillions of stars also containing solar systems, globular and galactic clusters, novae, and variable stars. Among the teeming multitudes of such gatherings of countless all-embracing galaxies, our own Milky Way system is just one. Even with the finest and latest equipment we can only dimly perceive some of the profusion of galaxies that abide in the universe. Hosts of island universes lie far beyond the reach of our feeble equipment and present faculties.

It is most fitting that the term *island universes* was first coined to describe galaxies by a famous German philosopher rather than an astronomer. It was used to define these remote other worlds by a genius who viewed the heavens with his mind's eye and not with a telescope. Immanuel Kant never traveled farther than sixty miles from the Prussian town where he was born in 1724. His vision extended far above the obvious. His original thinking can be compared to that of early Greeks like Plato and Aristotle. These were men whose visionary perceptions also reached beyond their own place and time.

Galaxy Types

Spiral

Elliptical

Barred spiral

As recently as one hundred years ago, the hazy patch in Triangulum near the constellation of Aries (to which Charles Messier had assigned the number 33) was thought to be a nearby nebula, a faint cloud of gas without much substance. It was the work of the American astronomer, Edwin Hubble, that allowed us to better set our sights. He studied certain variable stars that reveal their distance through periodic changes in brightness. Through such variables, Hubble was able to establish, in 1925, that what seemed like tenuous nearby nebulae were actually gigantic galaxies of countless suns far, far beyond our own Milky Way. Today we know that the distance to M33, the spiral in Triangulum, is on the order of 2.2 million light-years.

At this point it seems important to define the unit of *length,* not of time, that is expressed in the measurement of one light-year:

in 1 second light travels a distance of: . . . . 186,000 miles
in 1 minute (60 seconds) light travels: . . . . 11,160,000 miles
in 1 hour (60 minutes) light travels: . . . . 669,600,000 miles
in 1 day (24 hours) light travels: . . . . 16,070,400,000 miles
in 1 year (365 days) light travels: . . . . . . 5,865,696,000,000 miles
1 light-year equals about: . . . . 6,000,000,000,000 miles

In order to establish the distance to the spiral galaxy in Triangulum (M33), we must multiply two and two-tenths million light years by six trillion miles (1 light-year) to yield a distance of
13,200,000,000,000,000,000 miles
or 21,100,000,000,000,000,000 kilometers.
(In the shorthand of science this is expressed as 2.11×10^{19}.)

In order to sense the distance scale of the known universe, it seems very worthwhile to travel a few earth-miles or kilometers to a dark mountain site on a clear moonless night to try to glimpse with binoculars any of the galaxies listed above. It will become more revealing when we bear in mind that even at its mind-boggling range, M33 is regarded by astronomers as a member of our own "local group" of galaxies to which M31, the great galaxy in Andromeda, and our own Milky Way island also belong.

In time, the research of Edwin Hubble led to a momentous discovery that will bear the name *Hubble's law* forever. It established that the universe is constantly expanding. All galaxies keep moving away from one another at speeds that are proportional to their distances. Simply stated, this means that the farther out galaxies are, the faster they zoom away from each other and from us. Picture polka dots printed on a rapidly inflating balloon. Cosmologists now debate whether this expansion will continue indefinitely or will one day slow down and reverse itself.

Galaxies come in many different shapes and sizes. There are spirals and ellipticals. Some are seen edge-on, like Frisbees in flight; others resemble pinwheels. Many remain beyond observation, outside our optical perceptions. The fundamental realization of the incredible numbers, both in terms of distances and the sheer count of objects involved, must give any thinking person pause for thought. It seems impossible for intelligent beings on our planet not to contemplate the existence of extra-terrestrial intelligence, which science is just beginning to explore. To doubt or even to deny the possible presence of others somewhere, somehow, sometime, seems at least presumptuous if not conceited. Not only are there countless queries about the "where" and "how" that remain unanswered, but as yet innumerable questions remain unasked. We may not yet know how to address our inquiries concerning the "when" of time or the "where" of space.

As explained ("In the Beginning," page 12), we in the solar system have only about twenty-four thousand Genesis seconds—some seven hours of creation—left to ask and to answer all questions about time, nature, and their creator.

Project Taurus

The powerful and restless bull was an important part of ancient cultures in both religion and ceremonial magic. Taurus was the constellation that marked the vernal equinox from about 5000 B.C. to 2000 B.C. This was the golden age of ancient observational astrology, which gave birth to astronomy. We can easily find the celestial Taurus pictogram slightly to the left (east) and below (south) of the conspicuous galactic cluster M45 called the Pleiades, or popularly, "the seven sisters." Look for Taurus about 60 degrees above the southern compass point.

The constellation has a very bright anchor star on which to center the Starframe at the culmination dates and hours. It is the 0.9-magnitude star Aldebaran, also called Alpha (α) Tauri. When held 15–18 inches from the eye the Starframe is easily rotated on this beacon until the Pleiades and Aldebaran both overlap their counterparts in the sky. *Aldebaran,* translated from the Arabic, means "the Pleiades' follower." This is because when the galactic cluster M45 is observed rising above the eastern horizon, not far from the Zodiac sunrise position, Aldebaran follows close behind within one hour in right ascension (the Starframe is two hours wide in R.A.).

You will not be able to recognize the zodiacal starfields in their rising or setting positions until you have practiced following them down to the horizon from their highest positions in the sky. As with the sun, such times always precede or follow culmination by approximately six hours. Stellar pictograms turned on their sides appear foreshortened and are often difficult to recognize. That is why all first-time observations should be made at the southern culmination times and dates listed above. Practice discovering the Pleiades, which are easily recognizable from rising to setting. This will also help you familiarize yourself with constellations in relation to the planets that wander among them.

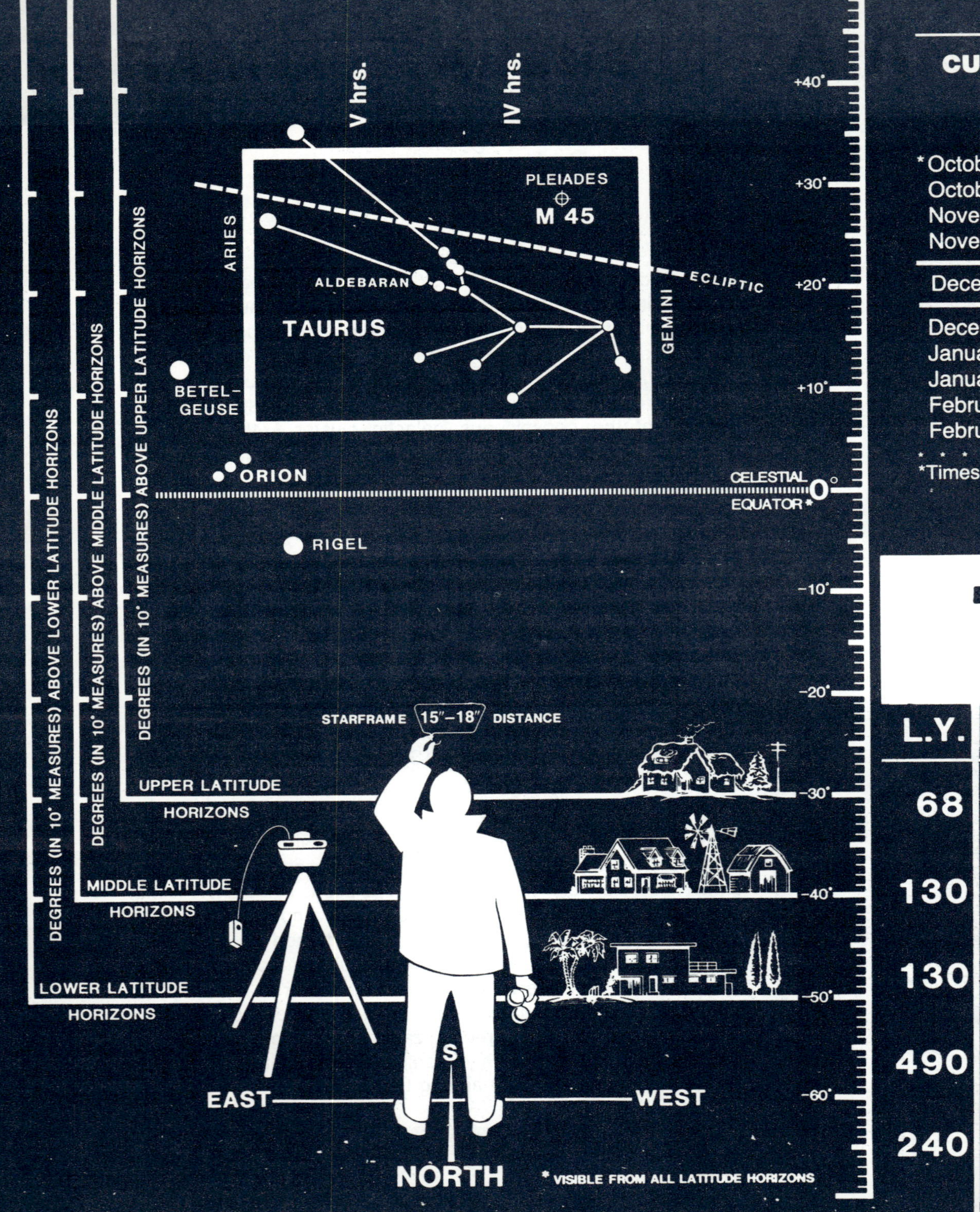

CULMINATION OF THE TAURUS STARFIELD
(see illustration on left)

Hold Starframe 15–18 inches from the eye

*October 1-October 15	at 5:00 am	= 05:00 hours
October 15-November 1	at 3:00 am	= 03:00 hours
November 1-November 15	at 2:00 am	= 02:00 hours
November 15-December 1	at 1:00 am	= 01:00 hours
December 1-December 15	at MIDNIGHT	= 24:00 hours
December 15-January 1	at 11:00 pm	= 23:00 hours
January 1-January 15	at 10:00 pm	= 22:00 hours
January 15-February 1	at 9:00 pm	= 21:00 hours
February 1-February 15	at 8:00 pm	= 20:00 hours
February 15-March 1	at 7:00 pm	= 19:00 hours

*Times on these dates are adjusted for daylight saving time.

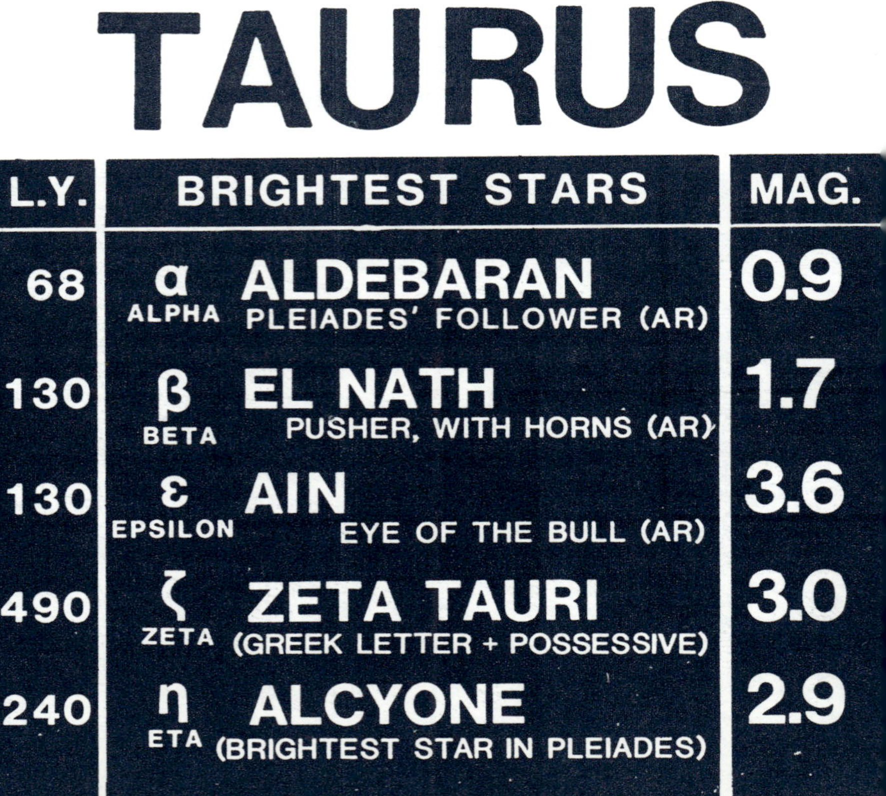

TAURUS

L.Y.	BRIGHTEST STARS	MAG.
68	α ALPHA — ALDEBARAN — PLEIADES' FOLLOWER (AR)	0.9
130	β BETA — EL NATH — PUSHER, WITH HORNS (AR)	1.7
130	ε EPSILON — AIN — EYE OF THE BULL (AR)	3.6
490	ζ ZETA — ZETA TAURI — (GREEK LETTER + POSSESSIVE)	3.0
240	η ETA — ALCYONE — (BRIGHTEST STAR IN PLEIADES)	2.9

There are only six to eight stars visible to the unaided eye in the Pleiades. A pair of binoculars may reveal ten times as many, depending on the quality of seeing from your chosen site. The brightest of the Pleiades stars is Alcyone at magnitude 2.9.

The *V*-shaped grouping of the Taurus stars is itself a nearby galactic cluster called *the Hyades.* They used to be called the "rainy stars." Their rising in autumn heralded the rainy season in Middle Eastern climates. It forms the "head of the bull" from which the long and straight horns point in a north-west direction.

There is only one other Messier object in Taurus. It forms the first entry in the Frenchman's catalogue. M1 is the faint remnant of a supernova that exploded in Taurus in A.D. 1054 and was recorded by Eastern astronomers. Chinese writings tell of a "guest star" that was so bright it could be seen in daytime. So cataclysmic was this stellar explosion that even today its remaining cloud of gas expands at the rate of some one thousand miles per second. You may not be able to see the Crab nebula M1 except in photographs of long exposures. (See back cover.)

The star Phi (Φ) Tauri is an "easy" double star that will reveal its components, of magnitudes 5 and 8.5, with optical aids. The variable star R in Taurus changes from magnitude 7.6 to invisibility of magnitude 14.7 and back again over a period of 324 days.

We have now completed 365 daily revolutions around the terrestrial merry-go-round of planet earth, while the celestial transparent carousel overhead has taken one complete turn, revealing the twelve zodiacal starfields. Don't get off. The journey is about to begin again as we reenter the constellation of Gemini and gain an ever better understanding of our place beneath the sun and under the stars.

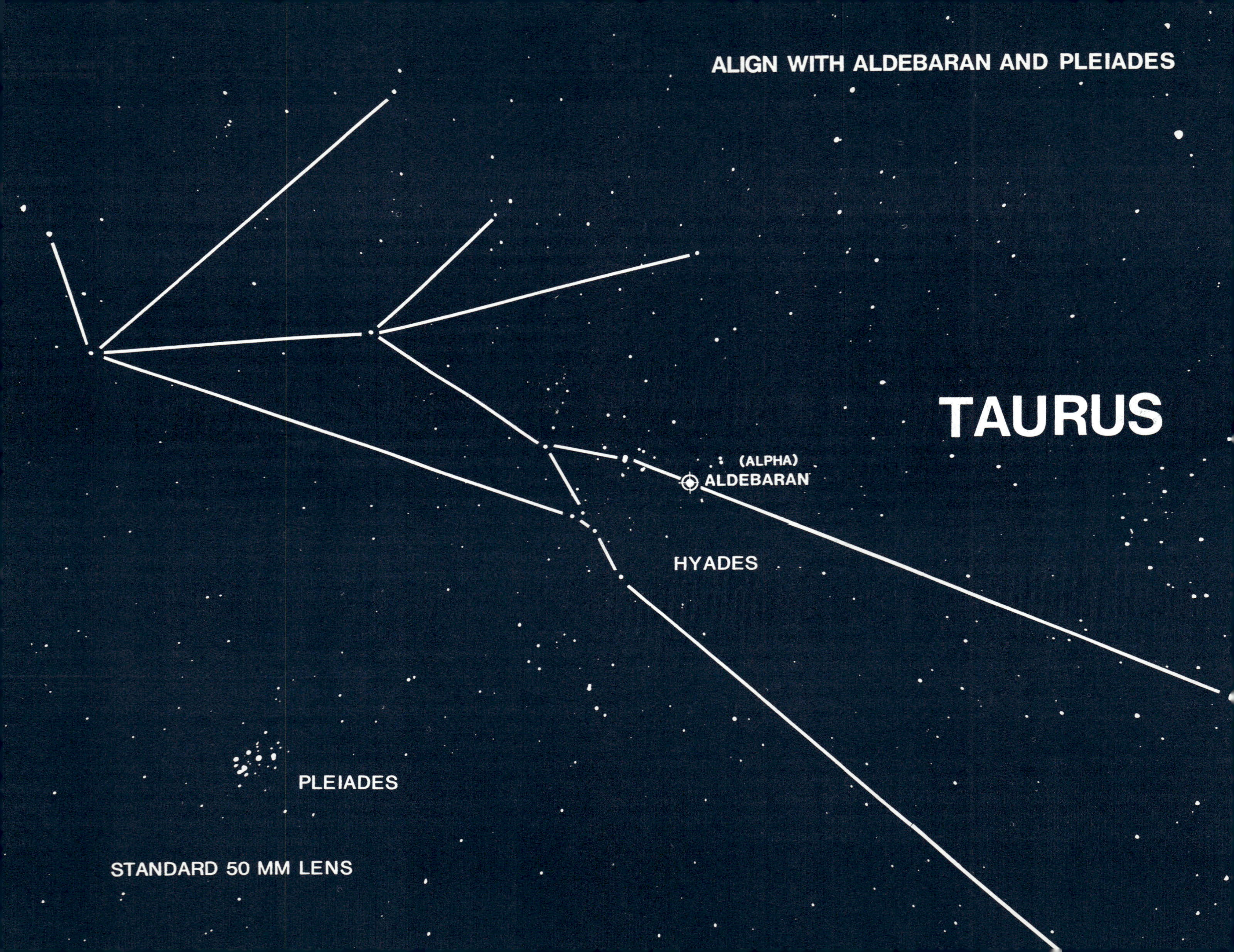

ALIGN WITH ALDEBARAN AND PLEIADES

TAURUS

(ALPHA)
ALDEBARAN

HYADES

PLEIADES

STANDARD 50 MM LENS

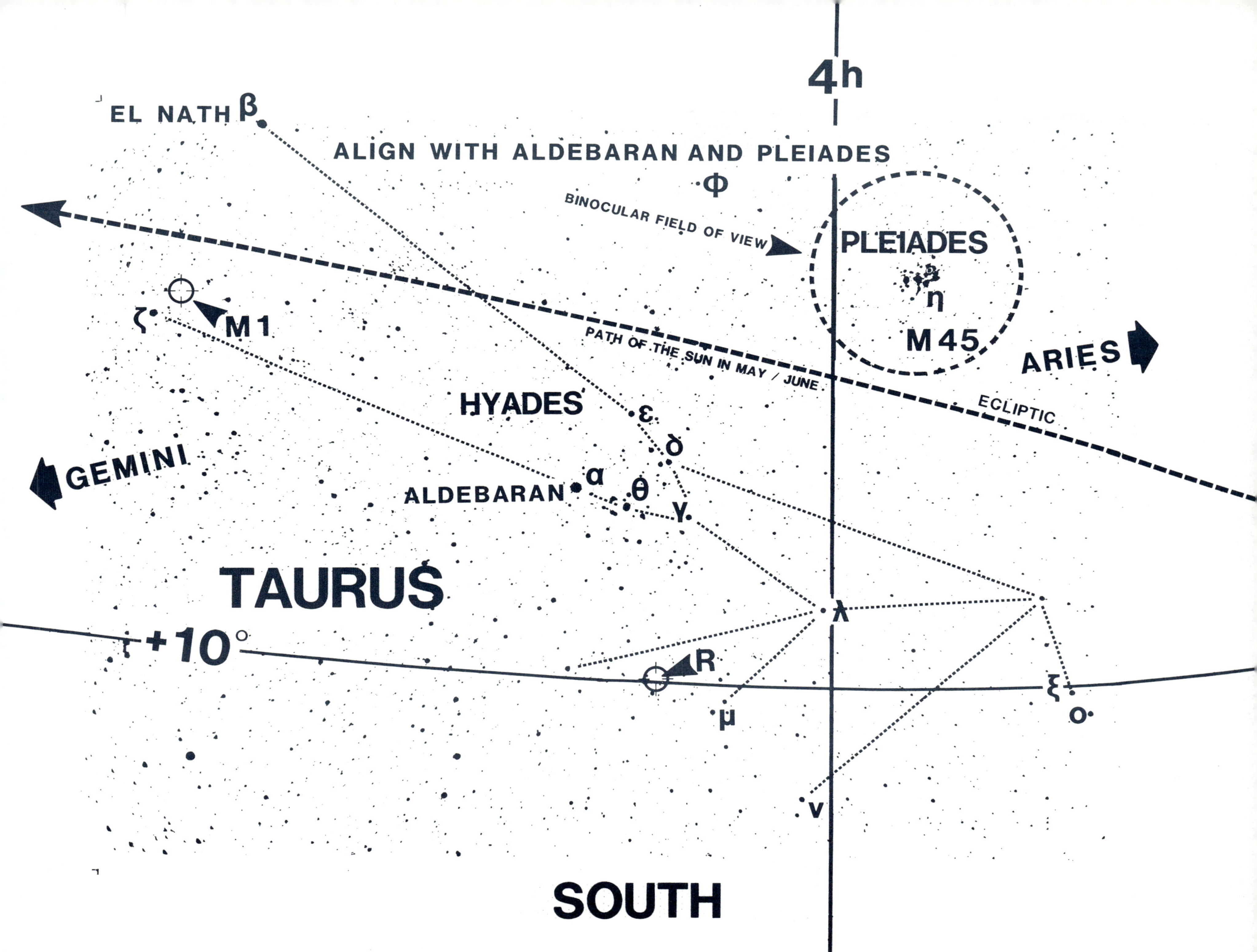
4h
EL NATH β
ALIGN WITH ALDEBARAN AND PLEIADES
Φ
BINOCULAR FIELD OF VIEW
PLEIADES
η
M45
ζ
M1
PATH OF THE SUN IN MAY / JUNE
ARIES
ECLIPTIC
HYADES
ε
δ
GEMINI
α
ALDEBARAN
θ
γ
TAURUS
λ
+10°
R
ξ
o
μ
v
SOUTH

Beyond Genesis

The roots of the words *astrology* and *astronomy* both relate to *astra,* the stars. It is in the letters affixed at the end of each word that we may look for specific meaning. *Astrology* refers to the oral or written expression, the doctrine or theory of the stars. Its suffix hails from the Greek word *logia,* meaning "words." Astrology is the word of the stars. *Astronomy,* on the other hand, refers to the system of laws governing the stars or the sum of knowledge regarding them. Its suffix also harks back to ancient Greece and the word *nomos,* which means "law." Astronomy can be called the law of the stars.

Beyond such self-evident semantic roots, four consonants set astro*log*y apart from astro*nom*y. The distinguishing letters are *L* and *G* together with *N* and *M.*

Let *L* stand for *light,* common to old Babylonian starwatchers and modern Mount Palomar cosmologists. You can look up the word *light* in any book on physics. We know exactly what light is. Or do we? As of now, the natural sciences cannot explain whether light is made up of waves or of matter. Should we picture gentle undulations like expanding ripples on a pond, or imagine fast baseballs zooming across an infield? If it is to be waves, then should we not ask scientists to arrest and pinpoint the exact location of light photons, or indicate the position of one tiny quantum among the "bundles of light" that are being discussed? Wave theories concerning light as electromagnetic radiation even address a so-called uncertainty principle. Science itself remains uncertain. If light takes the form of particular *quanta* (plural of *quantum*), then what about the established measures of the wavelengths of light? All the evidence points to the fact that light is *both* waves *and* particles. Science, which seeks—even demands—ultimate clear-cut truths, remains uncomfortable with this mysterious duality.

Another letter setting *astrology* apart from *astronomy* is the letter

G, as in *God.* You will rarely find this word in the pages of any book on science, let alone in scientific studies of the stars. It might seem that astronomers believe that if a creator is not written or talked about, the very idea of God will just fade away: no deity for atheist science or agnostic scientists.

Astrologers resort to similar word games, as we learned in discussing the natives of the constellation Cancer, for whom the term *Moonchildren* was substituted. No malignancies for horoscopists.

Similar parallels can be drawn with the remaining two letters, *N* and *M,* in the *-ology* and *-onomy* difference and the words connected with them. The letter *N* fittingly characterizes the term *noumenon.* Dictionaries define *noumena* (plural of *noumenon*) as "grounds of phenomena (plural of *phenomenon*) that are unknowable by the senses but remain conceivable by reason." Light, being visible, is a phenomenon, but its makeup has the properties of a noumenon. Whether God or the mere idea of God is a noumenon is a question that has preoccupied philosophers for the last Genesis second. This does not mean "since the beginning of time." As best we know, time began with the big bang, before which there was nothing, not even time. Epochs had no relevance.

The very *idea* of the noumenon called God has led to bloodshed and wars over many thousands of years, just as the mere *idea* of Nicolaus Copernicus cost the lives of countless souls before earth-turning, revolutionary concepts became universally accepted. Sadly, it was the church itself—the champion of God—that stood in the way of Copernican truth.

Today the word *God* does not even appear in the index of books on science (see Index, page 139). Is this in response to the infamous *Index Librorum Prohibitorum* of the Roman Catholic Church? The books on this list (there were a number of editions) were forbidden to be read by all but a few select people because the *ideas* in them were considered dangerous to faith and morals. Still, the revolution of mind and knowledge triumphed. Ideas of truth must and will prevail, even as they concern Hipparchus's discovery of the laws of precession, still largely ignored by sun-sign astrology today. Just as the mystery of planets traveling in retrograde motions was solved, pointing in time to Copernicus's ultimate discovery, so the question of the duality of light may one day be answered. Otherwise we could be confronted with another of the many mysteries which comprise our lives and our universe.

M is the last differentiating letter. It too is common to candlelit catacombs where occult horoscopes were cast and to floodlit lecture halls in which the latest scientific theories are presented. *M* stands for *mystery.* Once upon a time it may have denoted *miracle.* Let us face the facts: how can light be *both* particles *and* waves? How can such energy be two forces combined into one, or why? Is this a subtle sign of what nature holds in store for us; the yin and yang of ancient Eastern philosophies and beliefs? Can this duality be a first hint of what we may expect as we stand on the threshold of deep space? Is this one of the mysteries that await us as we are about to cross into the vacuum of the interstellar universe where particles are not supposed to be able to travel? How can this book on the stars not explain the much-vaunted mysterious black holes where gravity is so intense that even light itself is drawn into bottomless voids, never to escape or be seen again?

We may find the answer in the scriptures themselves. Years of study of the Hebrew language in the Holy Land have allowed me an understanding of the original text of the Bible, and the first part of Genesis in particular. If we combine biblical insight with astronomical outlook, the word of God may be reconciled with observable facts.

In the uncertain duality of the light of history, the noted Irish prelate James Ussher (1581–1656) set out to find the exact date of creation. This scholar, one of the most distinguished theologians of his day, established a system that determined the date of Genesis as having occurred in the year 4004 B.C.

The eighty-eighth word in Genesis can shed very clear light on the question, moving creation much further back in time. Eighteen billion years sounds very credible.

> In the beginning God created the heaven and the earth.
>
> And the earth was without form, and void; and darkness was upon the face of the deep. And the spirit of God moved upon the face of the waters.
>
> And God said, Let there be light: and there was light.
>
> And God saw the light, that it was good: and God divided the light from the darkness.
>
> And God called the light Day, and the darkness He called Night. And the evening and the morning were the *first* day.
> (emphasis mine)

These opening words of the Bible in the book of Genesis were translated into English from the ancient Masoretic Hebrew texts by the controversial early reformer William Tyndale. We know little about this cleric who was born "on the borders of Wales of uncertain parentage sometime between 1490 and 1495." But the date of the death of the theologian, who would be schooled at Oxford University, is branded in the parchments of time. On October 6 in the year 1536, at Vilvorde, the state prison of the Netherlands, he was strangled at the stake and his body afterwards burnt. The charge was heresy. Even Henry VIII could not save Tyndale from the fires of the Inquisition.

A letter from the condemned man to the governor of the prison still exists. In it, the doomed prisoner asks to be allowed the use of his Hebrew Bible, his grammar, and his dictionary. While Tyndale's familiarity with the Hebrew language has been questioned, the scholarship of this early translator of the Bible into English was admitted even by his adversaries. Still, Genesis, the first Book of Moses (chapter 1, verse 5), in what was to become the basis for the King James Version of the Bible, reveals an important departure from the original Hebrew text. It could hardly be called a willful perverting of the meaning of the scriptures, which might have justified the burning of Tyndale's books or the persecution of his person. However, a transposition in meaning of the eighty-eighth sacred word of God sheds important light on the dawning of our long-past morning in distant Genesis.

Today, the historic Hebrew tongue of the original scriptures has once more become a living language in the state of Israel. No longer are the lyrical words of the Psalms of King David confined to prayer books. They are sung and heard again in secular love songs from Galilee to Judea. Any bilingual child in today's Jerusalem would translate the last sentence in Genesis 1:5 to mean

> And there was evening and there was morning: *day one*

and not "the first day."

The eighty-eighth word can make a fundamental world of difference to the story of Genesis.

The elders of the large Jewish community in the German city of Worms, who may have assisted William Tyndale with Hebrew during his self-imposed exile from England, could have known the difference between the cardinal adjective *one* and the ordinal *first.* Martin Luther himself, perhaps the most influential reformer and translator of the Bible (into German), should then also have written

> *Da ward aus Abend und Morgen* ein Tag

and not *"der erste Tag"*

Correct choice and usage of words is central to any translation from one idiom to another. In transposing the meaning of tongues through time, other aspects might be considered: *Yom echad,* יוֹם אֶחָד where *yom* means "day" and the word *echad* stands for "one," could sequentially translate into "day one." The word for "first" would have been *rischon,* רִאשׁוֹן.

Reconstructing another possible original meaning, *yom echad* could even have been translated colloquially into "once upon a time." The Revised Standard Version of the Bible, published 1946, which in turn was a revision of the celebrated King James Bible of 1611 and is also based on Tyndale's works, reads: "And there was evening and there was morning, *one day*."

"One day" may not only be less in error than "the first day," it can also bear out more factual (or scientific) interpretations of the story of creation in Genesis. A word-for-word reading would have us believe that the entire world was created in six days, these being the first of the light and dark periods we still experience as days and nights. It can well be maintained that such days did not represent modern, standard twenty-four-hour periods, but rather geological ages of countless eternities, aeons measured in metaphorical days.

On such a basis, it is possible to establish that Genesis began with what today's cosmologists call the big bang some eighteen billion years ago. It becomes reasonable to suggest that although much has already been created, the process of creation is still going on. In terms of the incredible and the wondrous, Genesis—the beginning—has not yet ended.

"The first day," "day one," "one day," or "once upon a time;" which is it to be? Should we believe that for almost four hundred years, while the King James Bible was in uninterrupted use in the English-speaking world, the very opening chapter of the Book contained an error? That witnesses who laid their hands on such Bibles to swear to the truth before God gave testimony flawed with an imperfection? Are vows of marriage, for which old family Bibles are often brought into hallowed service, tainted by an error in translation perpetuated through time? How are we to reconcile this simple change in meaning with the outspoken emphasis of fundamentalism, which maintains that the Bible is "inerrant," that its word of God is without mistakes?

Only the staunchest and most conservative fundamentalists today would dare pit the Bible literally against the astronomical, geological, or evolutionary scientific truths.

In fundamentalist interpretations, this might soon force the admission that the word of God could be wrong. By translating the holy texts accurately while allowing freer interpretations of specific passages, we can safeguard credibility and maintain truth.

In our hearts and minds we are just starting to relate the infinity of space—and of Genesis—to our surroundings. We are setting out to explore ultimate frontiers. The cutting edge of science today speaks of time as the fourth dimension. To our three-dimensional ideas of north and south, east and west, in and out, we must add the mysterious dimension of time.

In this concept, nature's most magnificent free show offers more than we can ever see, even with the world's largest and costliest telescopes. You must draw on your own most important resources: your mind's eye and your soul. Here you may surpass what lies beyond the instruments of the world's leading scientists. Once you have been humbled by the realization that our entire solar system is but an insignificant part of the Milky Way galaxy, that what appears to us to be a fuzzy star is really a ball of a million suns, your horizons will expand to new dimensions. There need be no limit to your vision. Rereading the eighty-eighth word in the Bible may shed new light that will translate into what lay "beyond Genesis," once upon a time.

In my garden there are flowers that close their petals when the sun sets in the west. They reopen to full bloom soon after dawn with the coming light of the sun. This is a light–motion effect, first studied by Charles and Frances Darwin in 1881. There are other plants that turn their foliage sunward. They track the sun during the day just as a telescope tracks stars or a radar dish follows satellites. From sunrise to sunset such leaves are aimed toward the sun. During the night they assume a position of repose. Then, about an hour before sunrise, the leaves turn again to face the point on the eastern horizon where the sun came up the day before. This is called *heliotropism,* from the Greek *hēlios* ("sun") and *tropos* ("turn").

Professor Richard Willstätter was one of the luminaries performing similar research. He worked on the study of chlorophyll, the substance that turns plants green. For his unique discoveries he was awarded the 1915 Nobel Prize in chemistry. England recognized the German's brilliant achievements with an honorary doctorate from Oxford University. Germany bestowed its highest civilian honor, the noble order *Pour le Mérit,* on the gifted but humble scientist. Near the end of his lectures to students at the famous universities where he taught, the Nobel laureate would say, "I can tell you what happens when you mix an acid with a base, even demonstrate to you the salts which form in the chemical process. But I cannot answer the question *why* any of these things happen." He would conclude with the exhortation: *"Meine Damen und Herren, vergessen Sie das Wunder nicht."*

"Ladies and gentlemen, do not forget miracles."

METEORS

There is a relationship between the slow-moving glow of distant comets and the swift needle-sharp brilliance of Meteors, also called shooting stars. Mixed within the frosty mantle which may surround the core of large iceberg-sized comets are sand-grain-sized granules of rock. These leave invisible trails of debris in the comet's wake. Many, drawn earthward by gravity, enter our atmosphere from all directions. These fast-moving particles are heated by friction to where they briefly flare with incandescence before vaporizing at heights ranging from 100 to 150 miles. Such random meteors by themselves are called "sporadics." Larger pieces may make it down to the ground, in which case they are called "meteorites."

At certain times of the year, the earth in its journey around the sun coasts through the debris-littered orbit of a comet as shown on the right. On such occasions we encounter "Meteor showers," where dozens or even hundreds of shooting stars are visible in one hour. They give the appearance that they all originate from one point in the constellation after which the shower is named. This source, called the "radiant," is the result of an optical illusion much like the vanishing point of roads or telegraph poles coming from a great distance.

Photography of meteors is easy (pages 68-70) and can yield spectacular results. You will see the greatest number of shooting stars after midnight when the earth will have turned to where it "faces the meteor traffic." It can be compared to a car heading into the rain, with many more raindrops hitting the front windshield than the rear. Meteors shower down on earth at the rate of some 300 tons per day. Many fall into the oceans, and most are small. Some meteors are pieces of asteroids. Occasionally a major meteorite impact is reported in the media. The best known in the United States may be the meteor crater near Flagstaff, Arizona, which dates back to prehistoric times.

LEONID RADIANT

REGULUS

SHOWERS	DATES	MAXIMUM	METEORS†
Quadrantids	Jan. 1 - Jan. 5	Jan. 3 - 4	20 - 80
Alpha Aurigids	Jan. 15 - Feb. 20	Feb. 7 - 8	12
Zeta Bootids	Mar. 9 - Mar. 12	Mar. 10	10
Lyrids (April)	Apr. 19 - Apr. 24	Apr. 22	12
Eta Aquarids	May 1 - May 12	May 5	20
Lyrids (June)	June 10 - June 21	June 15	15
Delta Aquarids	July 15 - Aug. 15	July 28	35
PERSEIDS*	Aug. 1 - Aug. 15	Aug. 12*	65
Beta Cassiopeids	Sept. 7 - Sept. 15	Sept. 11	10
Orionids	Oct. 17 - Oct. 26	Oct. 20	35
LEONIDS*	Nov. 14 - Nov. 20	Nov. 17*	10-100
GEMINIDS*	Dec. 4 - Dec. 16	Dec. 13-14*	50

*Major meteor showers. Try not to miss these dates!
†Estimated number of meteors per hour over the entire sky.

ADAPTING TO THE DARK

Red cellophane candy wrappers are very useful tools in astronomy. For the following application any red translucent material will do, even some crimson tissue paper or cloth. Stretch it over the bulb of your flashlight with tape or a rubber band to cut down on the glare of white light. To read starframe charts at night, to make notes or to work a camera, always use such a red light source. It will help your eyes maintain their adaptation to the dark.

It takes our eyes a fair amount of time to get accustomed to the dark, as anyone knows who has ever tried to find a seat in a dark theater. We have learned from experience that after a few minutes our eyes adjust to the conditions and we are able to see what was hidden to us before.

In astronomy this wonderful natural gift is of greatest importance. Time and again a variety of conditions are blamed for the inability to see stars or a faint comet, when, in effect, impatience was the cause. It is simply impossible to go from a bright room into the night and to make observations (unless they involve the moon). At least ten or even fifteen minutes must be allowed for the eyes to become accustomed to the dark. City dwellers most of all should rest their eyes awhile in near-darkness. They will then be able to see stars of fainter magnitude than they considered possible.

Once this state of sensitivity has been achieved, even one brief look at a bright light or a television screen can spoil it, requiring a new period of readjustment for the eye. That is why the dimmed red flashlight is so important. Red light does not disturb the eye as much as white does.

In old cameras the aperture controlling the size of the lens opening was called the "iris" because it performs exactly the same function as the iris in the eye. Both regulate the amount of light which can pass through. Under bright conditions the pupils in our eyes protectively contract, just as we have to "stop down" lenses to avoid overexposures in bright sunlight.

At night, when our eyes are fully adapted to the dark, pupils are at their largest, admitting the maximum amount of light through the iris. At night, our camera lenses too must be set at their widest possible opening. We want to achieve maximum aperture for best night-seeing, both for our camera and for our eyes.

SKY CALENDAR JUNE 1991

An aid to enjoying the changing sky

Robert C. Victor, Jenny L. Pon, Robert D. Miller
ISSN 0733-6314

Use this scale to measure angular distances between objects on diagrams below.
0° 10° 20°

SUNDAY | MONDAY | TUESDAY | WEDNESDAY | THURSDAY | FRIDAY | SATURDAY

Sunday June 30, evening: Note how planets have rearranged their order since June 1, at far right.
Regulus in Leo • Venus • Mars • Jupiter • Castor • Pollux • Mercury • W • WNW

Calendar diagrams show sky from lat 40° N in middle of morning or evening twilight, about 50 min before sunrise or 50 min after sunset. Exceptions: June 28, 29; time as noted.

Observe the beautiful changing spectacle of planets in west at dusk—Venus, Mars, and Jupiter form most compact trio June 17. Compare June 1 at far right, June 30 at far left, and other dates below. Each night, backdrop of stars moves a little lower in the west; for example, note Gemini Twins (Pollux and Castor). Meanwhile all three planets move eastward, to upper left against zodiacal background. Brilliant **Venus** moves fastest, 27° during June 1-30, and overtakes both of the other planets. Faint **Mars** goes 17° and overtakes **Jupiter,** which shifts only 5°. **Mercury** emerges into evening sky by month's end; see June 30.

Magnitudes: Venus –4.1 to –4.3; **Jupiter** –1.9 to –1.8; **Saturn** +0.3 to +0.2; **Mars** +1.6 to +1.7; **Mercury** June 30, –0.7; **Uranus** 5.6; **Neptune** 7.9.

June 1 — Jupiter • Mars • Venus • Castor • Pollux • Twins. Saturday evening: Watch Venus' changing alignment with Twins in coming days. Procyon • W

2 — Morning: Face south. Waning gibbous Moon • Saturn

3 — Morning: Moon • Saturn in south

4 — Evening: Jupiter • Mars • Venus • Twins • Procyon • W • WNW

5 — Moon at Last Quarter, 90° (¼ circle) west of Sun in morning sky. Look before and after sunrise.

6 — Mars in Beehive Cluster tonight and tomorrow night. Use binoculars around end of evening twilight.

7 — Evening: Jupiter • Mars • Venus • Twins • Procyon • W • WNW

8 — Mars at aphelion, 1.67 a.u. from Sun. Mars won't be this far from Sun again until April 25, 1993.

9 — Morning: Moon • Pleiades • ENE

10 — Morning: Moon • Pleiades • ENE

11 — This week **Uranus** passes 3.1° N of 2nd-mag Sigma Sagittarii in handle of Teapot. **Neptune** is 3.6° ENE of Uranus and 0.6° S of 3rd-mag Pi.
Morning: Pleiades • Old Moon • ENE

12 — New Moon 8:06 a.m. EDT (5:06 a.m. PDT).
Evening: Venus in N edge of Beehive. Mars-Jupiter less than 1° apart June 12-15.

13 — Ma • Ve • Ju. Ve = Venus; Ma = Mars; Ju = Jupiter. Evening: Ve at greatest elongation, 45° E of Sun. Ma-Ju closest, 0.6° apart. Twins • Young Moon • WNW

14 — Ma • Ve • Ju • Moon • Twins. Evening: Ma-Ju still 0.7° apart. WNW

15 — Evening: Moon • Ma • Ve • Ju • W

16 — Mercury at superior conjunction (beyond Sun) tonight. Evening: Regulus • Moon • Ma • Ju • Ve. Ve-Ju less than 2° apart June 16-19.

Monday 17, evening: Ma • Ve • Ju. 3 planets within 1.8° field: Rare compact gathering of three naked-eye planets in dark sky! Twins • W • WNW

Tues 18 — Moon passes First Quarter tonight. It is 90° (¼ circle) east of Sun and appears half full in evening sky.

Wednesday 19, evening: Ma • Ve • Ju • Twins • WNW

Evenings: Venus-Mars less than 1° apart June 20-26.
Mornings: Spica in SSW • Moon Fri June 21 • Moon Thurs June 20

Friday June 21 — Solstice 5:19 p.m. EDT; summer begins. Sun enters Gemini.
Regulus in Leo

Saturday evening, June 22: Mars only ⅓° lower left of Venus. Ve • Ma • Ju • Twins • W • WNW

Sunday evening, June 23: Venus-Mars appear closest, 0.2° apart; Jupiter 4° to their lower right. Moon near head of Scorpius; see next box right.

Sunday evening, June 30: See box at top left corner of this calendar.

24 — Evenings: Moon, Sunday June 23 • Moon Monday, June 24 • Antares • SSE

25 — Regulus • Ve • Ma • Ju. Evening: W

26 — Penumbral lunar eclipse (undetectable) 11:15 p.m. EDT. Tonight's Moon is most distant of 1991. Evening: Lambda Sagittarii, top of Teapot • Full Moon • SE

27 — Evening: Lambda Sgr • Moon • SE

28 — Two hours after sunset: Moon • Saturn • ESE

29 — Morning: Saturn in SSW, only 4° upper left of Moon.
Two hours after sunset: Saturn • Moon • ESE

CURRENT SKY INFORMATION
Call (517) 332-STAR

Planets next month: In July 1991, the evening planet spectacle goes on — Mercury, Venus, Mars, and Jupiter all continue eastward against background stars. **Venus** and **Mars** linger close to each other **in Leo** all month, gradually spreading from 2° apart on July 1 to 6° apart on July 31. On the evenings of July 9 and 10, Venus, Mars, and Regulus (Leo's brightest star) fit into a field just over 3° across as Venus slides less than 1° south of the star. The arrangement of the Sun and four planets on the next day is shown on our **all-sky chart for the July 11 total eclipse of the Sun,** next page. It shows Venus-Mars-Regulus still tightly grouped, and **Mercury** closing in on **Jupiter.** A few evenings later, on July 14, Mars passes 0.6° north of Regulus, and Mercury comes exceedingly close to Jupiter. Venus attains greatest brilliancy in mid-July as it swings closer to Earth and presents a broad crescent through telescopes. Mercury swings out from Sun's far side to attain greatest elongation, 25° E of Sun, on July 25. That evening, the speedy planet is seen 1.7° south of Regulus. Meanwhile, slow Jupiter has been left behind and is just about lost in the glare of the approaching Sun. **Saturn,** in Capricornus, is at opposition to the Sun on July 26 and culminates in the middle of the night. Thus it does not appear on our July daytime chart.

The Sky During Totality

Total Eclipse of the Sun
July 11, 1991

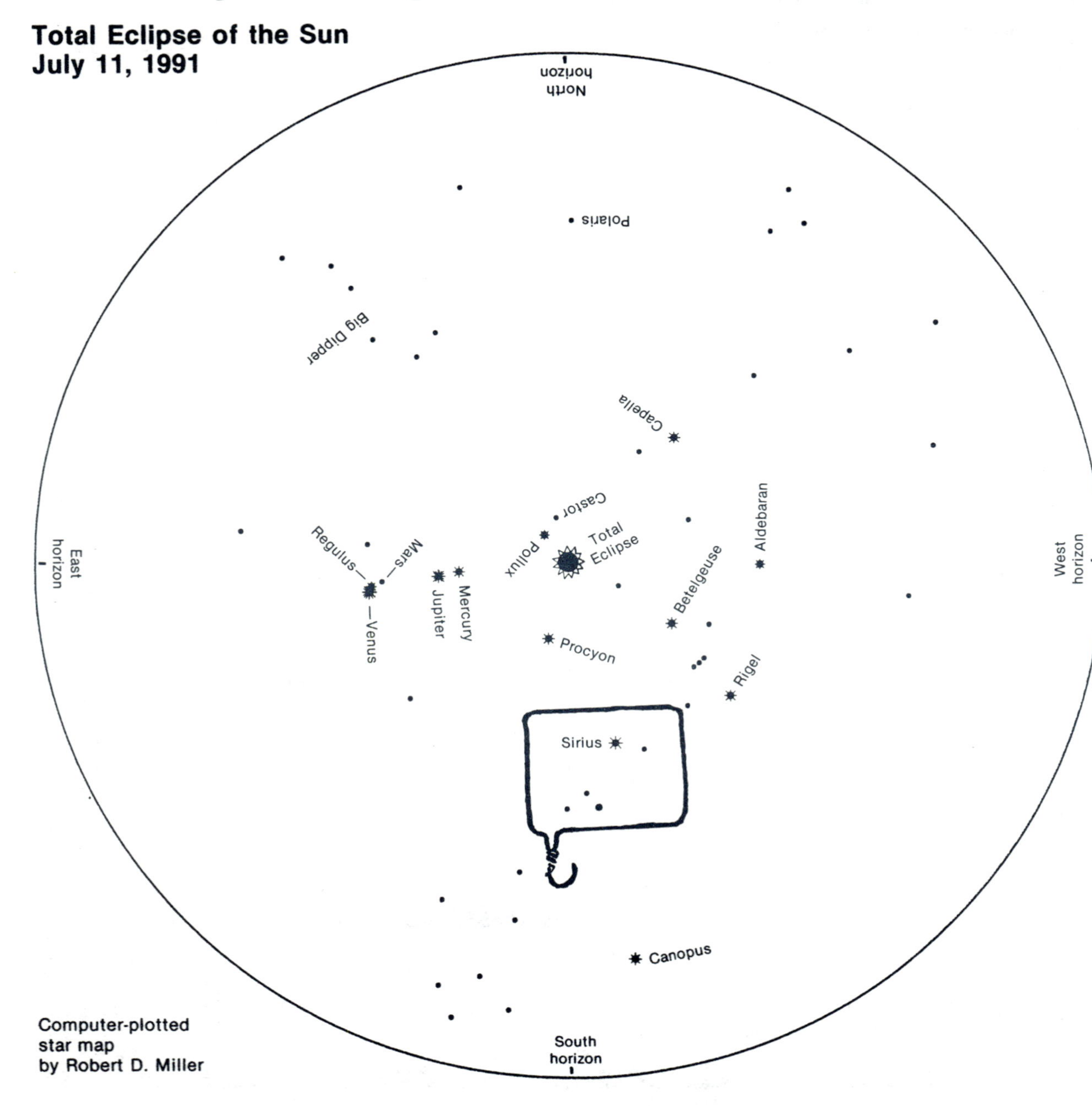

Computer-plotted star map by Robert D. Miller

On July 11, 1991, a total eclipse of the Sun will be visible within a strip up to 261 km (162 mi) wide, across the Eastern Pacific Ocean, all of the Island of Hawaii, and portions of Mexico, Central America, Colombia, and Brazil. In western Mexico, the Sun will be totally eclipsed for as long as 6 minutes 58 seconds, the longest total solar eclipse until June 25, 2150.

This chart shows the entire sky visible at mid-totality from longitude 105.2° west, latitude 22.0° north, at 12:06 p.m. Mountain Standard Time, just after the center of the Moon's shadow attains landfall on the Mexican mainland's west coast. From that location, the totally eclipsed Sun is almost exactly overhead.

Venus, near greatest brilliancy, gleams 41° to the east of the Sun. The 1.4-magnitude star **Regulus** in Leo, and 1.8-magnitude **Mars,** can be spotted to the northwest of Venus by about 1° and 3°, respectively. Very bright **Jupiter** (magnitude −1.7) is 14° west of Venus, or one-third of the way from Venus back toward the Sun. Zero-magnitude **Mercury** can be seen another 4° sunward (west) of Jupiter.

On this chart, all stars of magnitude 2.5 or brighter are plotted; this is the faintest limit that might be seen with the unaided eye at mid-totality in this unusually long eclipse. All stars of first magnitude or brighter are labeled, as well as the planets and selected additional stars.

Note Pollux and Castor, the Gemini Twins, within 8° to 10° northeast of the overhead Sun.

Far to the south of the Sun, a **STARFRAME**® is superimposed on the constellation Canis Major, which has just passed culmination.

This same sky, excluding planets, can be seen in the middle of the night at the opposite time of year — January — or during evening hours in February and March. But from middle northern latitudes, the entire starfield would be shifted southward: Polaris would appear higher in the northern sky, Pollux and Castor would shift to south of overhead, Sirius in Canis Major would be lower in the south, and Canopus would drop below the southern horizon.

Subscribers to the Abrams Planetarium **Sky Calendar** will note, on the reverse side of each monthly calendar sheet, a map of the evening sky. More detailed than the daytime chart shown here, the evening sky maps plot and label such star groups as the Big and Little Dippers, Leo, Orion, Canis Major and Canis Minor, the Hyades and Pleiades clusters in Taurus, and positions of a few deep-sky objects. The maps are useful for a wide range of middle northern latitudes.

A subscription to the monthly **Sky Calendar** (including the **Evening Skies** maps) may be started anytime. Order from Abrams Planetarium, Michigan State University, East Lansing, Michigan, 48824 USA. Cost (in 1988) is US $6 per year in North America, $11 elsewhere. Or clip out the coupon on the last page of this book and send it in with a self-addressed stamped envelope to receive a free sample current issue.

—Robert C. Victor

Planet Positions 1988–2000

Only three of the bright major planets need concern us when we seek out the constellations near their culminating "summit" positions as listed in the chart on pages 10–11. Only Mars, Jupiter, and Saturn can reach such crowning positions in or near your Starframes during hours of darkness. Don't allow these bright wanderers to mislead you. In fact, by familiarizing yourself with the constellations, you will be able to observe their gradually changing positions as they journey among the stars in the band of the Zodiac. Planets sometimes travel above, and at other times below the "ecliptic," the line marked in all our pictograms. Listed here are the constellations of the Zodiac in which planets may be seen now and through the year 2000. Be on the lookout for these dazzlers. When in doubt about a very bright "star" which is not shown in the pictograms, check the following tables which will easily and quickly identify the heavenly roamers from tonight through the end of this century. Probably the breathtaking "star" is a planet. Sometimes two of them together travel in or near your Starframe. These tables were compiled by Jenny Pon of Abrams Planetarium, Michigan State University (see the Sky Calendar on page 131).

Key to Constellations

GEM = Gemini		SGR = Sagittarius	
CNR = Cancer		CAP = Capricornus	
LEO = Leo		AQR = Aquarius	
VIR = Virgo		PSC = Pisces	
LIB = Libra		ARI = Aries	
SCO = Scorpius		TAU = Taurus	

Compiled by Jenny Pon, Abrams Planetarium, Michigan State University

1988

	JAN	FEB	MAR	APR	MAY	JUN	JUL	AUG	SEP	OCT	NOV	DEC
MARS	Lib/Sco	Sco/Sgr	Sgr	Sgr/Cap	Cap/Aqr	Aqr/Psc	Psc	Psc	Psc	Psc	Psc	Psc
JUPITER	Psc	Psc	Psc/Ari	Ari	Ari	Ari/Tau	Tau	Tau	Tau	Tau	Tau	Tau
SATURN	Sco/Sgr	Sgr	Sgr	Sgr	Sgr	Sgr	Sgr	Sgr/Sco	Sco/Sgr	Sgr	Sgr	Sgr

1989

	JAN	FEB	MAR	APR	MAY	JUN	JUL	AUG	SEP	OCT	NOV	DEC
MARS	Psc/Ari	Ari	Tau	Tau/Gem	Gem	Gem/Cnr	Cnr/Leo	Leo	Leo/Vir	Vir	Vir/Lib	Lib/Sco
JUPITER	Tau	Tau	Tau	Tau	Tau	Tau	Tau/Gem	Gem	Gem	Gem	Gem	Gem
SATURN	Sgr	Sgr	Sgr	Sgr	Sgr	Sgr	Sgr	Sgr	Sgr	Sgr	Sgr	Sgr

1990

	JAN	FEB	MAR	APR	MAY	JUN	JUL	AUG	SEP	OCT	NOV	DEC
MARS	Sco/Sgr	Sgr	Sgr/Cap	Cap/Aqr	Aqr/Psc	Psc	Psc/Ari	Ari/Tau	Tau	Tau	Tau	Tau
JUPITER	Gem	Gem	Gem	Gem	Gem	Gem	Gem	Gem/Cnr	Cnr	Cnr	Cnr	Cnr
SATURN	Sgr	Sgr	Sgr	Sgr	Sgr	Sgr	Sgr	Sgr	Sgr	Sgr	Sgr	Sgr

1991

	JAN	FEB	MAR	APR	MAY	JUN	JUL	AUG	SEP	OCT	NOV	DEC
MARS	Tau	Tau	Tau	Tau/Gem	Gem/Cnr	Cnr/Leo	Leo	Leo/Vir	Vir	Vir/Lib	Lib	Sco
JUPITER	Cnr	Cnr	Cnr	Cnr	Cnr	Cnr	Cnr/Leo	Leo	Leo	Leo	Leo	Leo
SATURN	Sgr	Sgr/Cap	Cap	Cap	Cap	Cap	Cap	Cap	Cap	Cap	Cap	Cap

1992

	JAN	FEB	MAR	APR	MAY	JUN	JUL	AUG	SEP	OCT	NOV	DEC
MARS	Sco/Sgr	Sgr/Cap	Cap/Aqr	Aqr/Psc	Psc	Psc/Ari	Ari/Tau	Tau	Tau/Gem	Gem	Gem	Gem
JUPITER	Leo	Leo	Leo	Leo	Leo	Leo	Leo	Leo	Leo/Virgo	Vir	Vir	Vir
SATURN	Cap	Cap	Cap	Cap	Cap	Cap	Cap	Cap	Cap	Cap	Cap	Cap

1993

	JAN	FEB	MAR	APR	MAY	JUN	JUL	AUG	SEP	OCT	NOV	DEC
MARS	Gem	Gem	Gem	Gem/Cnr	Cnr	Cnr/Leo	Leo	Leo/Vir	Vir	Vir/Lib	Lib/Sco	Sco/Sgr
JUPITER	Vir	Vir	Vir	Vir	Vir	Vir	Vir	Vir	Vir	Vir	Vir	Vir/Lib
SATURN	Cap	Cap	Cap	Cap/Aqr	Aqr	Aqr	Aqr	Aqr/Cap	Cap	Cap	Cap	Cap

1994

	JAN	FEB	MAR	APR	MAY	JUN	JUL	AUG	SEP	OCT	NOV	DEC
MARS	Sgr/Cap	Cap	Cap/Aqr	Aqr/Psc	Psc/Ari	Ari/Tau	Tau	Tau/Gem	Gem	Cnr	Cnr/Leo	Leo
JUPITER	Lib	Lib	Lib	Lib	Lib/Vir	Vir	Vir	Vir/Lib	Lib	Lib	Lib	Lib/Sco
SATURN	Cap/Aqr	Aqr	Aqr	Aqr	Aqr	Aqr	Aqr	Aqr	Aqr	Aqr	Aqr	Aqr

1995

	JAN	FEB	MAR	APR	MAY	JUN	JUL	AUG	SEP	OCT	NOV	DEC
MARS	Leo	Leo/Cnr	Cnr	Cnr/Leo	Leo	Leo	Leo/Vir	Vir	Vir/Lib	Lib/Sco	Sco/Sgr	Sgr
JUPITER	Sco	Sco	Sco	Sco	Sco	Sco	Sco	Sco	Sco	Sco	Sco	Sco/Sgr
SATURN	Aqr	Aqr	Aqr	Aqr	Aqr/Psc	Psc	Psc	Psc	Psc/Aqr	Aqr	Aqr	Aqr

1996

	JAN	FEB	MAR	APR	MAY	JUN	JUL	AUG	SEP	OCT	NOV	DEC
MARS	Sgr/Cap	Cap/Aqr	Aqr/Psc	Psc	Ari	Ari/Tau	Tau/Gem	Gem	Gem/Cnr	Cnr/Leo	Leo	Leo/Vir
JUPITER	Sgr	Sgr	Sgr	Sgr	Sgr	Sgr	Sgr	Sgr	Sgr	Sgr	Sgr	Sgr
SATURN	Aqr/Psc	Psc	Psc	Psc	Psc	Psc	Psc	Psc	Psc	Psc	Psc	Psc

1997

	JAN	FEB	MAR	APR	MAY	JUN	JUL	AUG	SEP	OCT	NOV	DEC
MARS	Vir	Vir	Vir/Leo	Leo	Leo	Leo/Vir	Vir	Vir/Lib	Lib	Sco	Sco/Sgr	Sgr/Cap
JUPITER	Sgr/Cap	Cap	Cap	Cap	Cap	Cap	Cap	Cap	Cap	Cap	Cap	Cap
SATURN	Psc	Psc	Psc	Psc	Psc	Psc	Psc	Psc	Psc	Psc	Psc	Psc

1998

	JAN	FEB	MAR	APR	MAY	JUN	JUL	AUG	SEP	OCT	NOV	DEC
MARS	Cap/Aqr	Aqr/Psc	Psc	Psc/Ari	Ari/Tau	Tau	Tau/Gem	Gem/Cnr	Cnr/Leo	Leo	Leo/Vir	Vir
JUPITER	Cap/Aqr	Aqr	Aqr	Aqr	Aqr/Psc	Psc	Psc	Psc	Psc/Aqr	Aqr	Aqr	Aqr/Psc
SATURN	Psc	Psc	Psc	Psc	Psc/Ari	Ari	Ari	Ari	Ari	Ari	Ari/Psc	Psc

1999

	JAN	FEB	MAR	APR	MAY	JUN	JUL	AUG	SEP	OCT	NOV	DEC
MARS	Vir	Vir/Lib	Lib	Lib/Vir	Vir	Vir	Vir/Lib	Lib	Lib/Sco	Sco/Sgr	Sgr/Cap	Cap
JUPITER	Psc	Psc	Psc	Psc	Psc	Psc/Ari	Ari	Ari	Ari	Ari	Ari/Psc	Psc
SATURN	Psc	Psc/Ari	Ari	Ari	Ari	Ari	Ari	Ari	Ari	Ari	Ari	Ari

2000

	JAN	FEB	MAR	APR	MAY	JUN	JUL	AUG	SEP	OCT	NOV	DEC
MARS	Aqr	Aqr/Psc	Psc/Ari	Ari/Tau	Tau	Tau/Gem	Gem/Cnr	Cnr/Leo	Leo	Leo/Vir	Vir	Vir
JUPITER	Psc	Psc/Ari	Ari	Ari	Ari	Tau	Tau	Tau	Tau	Tau	Tau	Tau
SATURN	Ari	Ari	Ari	Ari	Ari	Ari/Tau	Tau	Tau	Tau	Tau	Tau	Tau

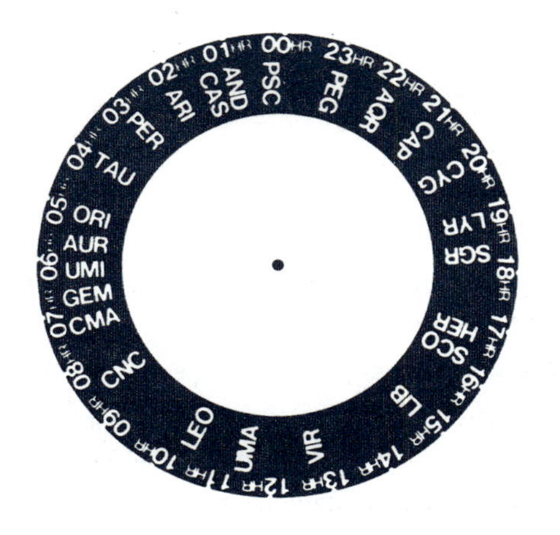

Resources

Bibliography and Recommended Reading

Kukarkin, B. V., and others, *Catalogues of Variable Stars,* 3 volumes and supplement. Moscow: USSR National Academy of Sciences, 1976.

Kunitzsch, Paul, *Arabische Sternnamen in Europa.* Wiesbaden, Germany: Otto Harrassowitz, 1959.

Liller, Bill, and Ben Mayer, *The Cambridge Astronomy Guide.* Cambridge, England: Cambridge University Press, 1985.

Mallas, J. H., and E. Kreimer, *The Messier Album.* Cambridge, MA: Sky Publishing Corporation, 1978.

Mayer, Ben, *Starwatch.* New York: Perigee Books, 1984.

Menzel, D. H., and J. M. Pasachoff, *A Field Guide to the Stars and Planets,* 2nd edition. Boston: Houghton Mifflin, 1983.

Vehrenberg, Hans, *Atlas of Deep Sky Splendors.* Cambridge, MA: Sky Publishing Corporation, 1978.

Telescopes and Related Equipment

Bushnell/Bausch & Lomb
135 Prestige Park Circle
East Hartford, CT 06108

Celestron International
2835 Columbia Street, Torrance, CA 90503

Meade Instruments Corporation
1675 Toronto Way, Costa Mesa, CA 92626

Orion Telescope Center
421 Soquel Avenue, Santa Cruz, CA 95062
(408) 458-9090

Questar Corporation
P.O. Box C, New Hope, PA 18938

Sky Calendar (Monthly/Daily)
Abrams Planetarium
Michigan State University, East Lansing, MI 48824

Starframes/Stellaphanes
Starwatcher's Decoder Set
Bausch & Lomb, Bushnell Division
300 North Hill Avenue, San Dimas, CA 91773

STELAS
Orion Telescope Center
421 Soquel Avenue, Santa Cruz, CA 95062
(408) 458-9090

Magazines

Astronomy/Deep Sky/Telescope Making
Astromedia, Kalmbach Publishing Company
1027 North Seventh Street, Milwaukee, WI 53233

Griffith Observer
Griffith Park Observatory
2800 East Observatory Road, Los Angeles, CA 90027

Mercury
Astronomical Society of the Pacific
1290 24th Avenue, San Francisco, CA 94122

Sky and Telescope
Sky Publishing Corporation
49 Bay State Road, Cambridge, MA 02238

Sky Calendar
Abrams Planetarium
Michigan State University
East Lansing, MI 48824

Star Atlases

A.A.V.S.O. Variable Star Atlas
American Association of Variable Star Observers
25 Birch Street, Cambridge, MA 02138

Norton's Star Atlas
Sky Publishing Corporation
49 Bay State Road, Cambridge, MA 02238

Tirion Atlas 2000.0
Sky Publishing Corporation
49 Bay State Road, Cambridge, MA 02238

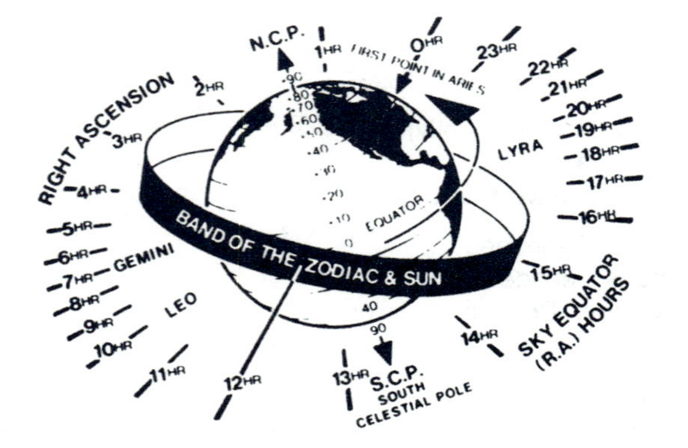

Glossary

A.A.V.S.O. American Association of Variable Star Observers.

APERTURE. Effective light-gathering diameter such as the opening of a lens.

ASTEROID. A minor planet.

BLINK COMPARISON. A method for astronomical discovery employing two photographs taken at different times and or dates.

BLINK COMPARATOR. An optical or electronic device permitting the easy comparison of reference and data images for astronomical discovery.

CELESTIAL EQUATOR. A great circle on the celestial sphere beyond and in the same plane as the equator of the earth.

COMET. A body of ices, rock, and dusty matter.

CONSTELLATION. A grouping of stars named for mythical figures, animals, or objects.

COORDINATE. Designation of a space location derived from its position in relation to celestial longitude and latitude.

CULMINATION. Point of highest position of objects in the sky.

DAYLIGHT SAVING TIME. Time more advanced by one hour than standard time.

DECLINATION (Dec). The angle north or south of the equator to an object measured from the twenty-four-hour circle of the celestial equator.

ECLIPSE. The partial or complete cutting off of the light of a body by another passing in front of it.

ECLIPTIC. The apparent sky path of the sun.

EQUATORIAL DRIVE. A motorized mounting with an axis parallel to the earth's axis whose motion compensates for the rotation of our planet.

EQUINOX. One of the two intersections of the ecliptic and the celestial equator.

FLATFORM. A seemingly flat observing platform on the surface of the round earth.

GALACTIC CLUSTER. An "open" cluster of stars located within the disk of our galaxy.

GALAXY. A vast assemblance of millions to hundreds of thousands of millions of stars.

GENESIS SECOND. A time span of approximately 200,000 years based on estimates of the age of our universe.

GLOBULAR CLUSTER. Ball-shaped groupings of stars above and below the galactic plane.

GOD. The ultimate reality, the infinite mind, The Creator, Gen. 1:2.

HAYSTACK. Horizon zones of haystack shape centered on the ecliptic, where comets can be found before sunrise and/or after sunset.

INDEX LIBRORUM PROHIBITORUM. The official list of books forbidden to all members of the Roman Catholic Church except cardinals, bishops and ordinaries. There have been many editions of the *Index.* The books on this list were those that had been judged dangerous to faith and morals. Anyone could apply to the Holy Office for permission to read them. The *Index* was abolished in 1966 by Pope Paul VI.

LATITUDE. A north-south coordinate on the surface of the earth.

LIGHT-YEAR. A measure of distance, not time. The distance light travels in one year.

LIGHT POLLUTION. A loss of blackness of night caused by manmade illumination.

LONGITUDE. Angular distance measured on a great terrestrial or celestial circle.

MAGNITUDE. A scale of measurement for the brightness of stars and other sky objects.

METEOR. A body of rock or metal heated to incandescence when it enters the atmosphere of the earth. Also called a "shooting star."

METEORITE. Surviving part of a meteor which strikes the earth after a fiery descent.

METEOR SHOWER. A display of many meteors radiating from a common point in the sky.

MILKY WAY. A wide band of light stretching around the celestial sphere caused by the light of myriads of faint stars.

NEBULA. A cloud of interstellar gas or dust glowing from or reflecting nearby starlight.

NOUMENON (plural NOUMENA). A phenomenon which is not knowable by the senses but is conceivable by reason (*see also* phenomenon).

NOVA. A star that suddenly undergoes an outburst of radiant energy and increases its luminosity by hundreds or thousands of times.

OPEN CLUSTER. See Galactic Cluster.

ORBIT. The path of a body in its revolution about another body or center of gravity.

PHENOMENON (plural PHENOMENA). An observable fact or event; something that is known through the senses, rather than by thought or intuition; a rare fact or event.

PLANET. One of nine large spherical objects revolving about the sun and shining by the reflected light of the sun.

PLANETARY NEBULA. A shell of gas blasted from a dying star.

PRECESSION. A cone-shaped motion of the axis of the earth's rotation caused mostly by the sun and the moon.

PROBLICOM. A PROjection BLInk COMparator to present two different photographs of the same region of the sky for easy comparison.

RADIANT. The point on the celestial sphere from which meteors of a given shower seem to originate.

RETROGRADE MOTION. Apparent "backward" (or westward) drift of a planet on the celestial sphere with respect to the stars, resulting from the motion of the earth.

RIGHT ASCENSION (R.A.) A coordinate for finding the east-west positions of celestial bodies, measuring eastward along the celestial equator from the spring equinox to the point below or above the body in question.

SCALE. The linear distance in a photograph corresponding to a particular angular distance in the sky, i.e., so many fractions of an inch per arc-minute or per degree.

SERENDIPITY. The gift of finding valuable or useful things or data not sought for.

SOLSTICE. One of the two points on the ecliptic when and where the sun reaches its maximum distance north and south of the celestial equator.

SPORADIC METEOR. A meteor (shooting star) that does not belong to a meteor shower.

STARFRAME. A sky area defined by a specific outline (such as a bent coathanger) to contain the principal stars of a constellation for easy repeated finding and study.

STAR PARTY. A gathering of amateur star-lovers on new-moon weekend nights to view the skies, take photographs, compare equipment and share astronomical information.

STEBLICOM. A STEreo BLInk COMparator, the least complicated and simplest discovery device for photograph comparison.

STELAS. A Stop The Earth, Lock All Stars motor driven device to compensate for equatorial revolution with minimal means.

SUPERNOVA. A stellar cataclysm in which a star explodes, briefly increasing its luminosity by hundreds of thousands to hundreds of millions of times.

TERMINATOR. The dividing line between the sunlit and shadowed portions of the moon or a planet.

VARIABLE STAR. A star whose brightness varies.

VIBLICOM. A patented electro-optical device to achieve Blink Comparison through video technology; a VIdeo BLInk COMparator.

ZENITH. The point directly overhead, the direction opposite to that of a plumb bob.

ZODIAC. A band around the sky which has the ecliptic in its center and in which the sun, moon, and planets move.

Index

Starwatcher's Special Offer

____
Name

____
Address

____
City State Zip

YES! Please send me my STARWATCHER'S DECODER SET at the SPECIAL OFFER price of only $22.95, plus shipping and handling.

Number of Kits ordered _____ X $22.95 . . . . $_______

California residents only add $1.49 each Sales Tax . . . . $_______

Shipping and handling $3.95 each . . . . $_______

TOTAL $_______

Check, money order, VISA or MasterCard. Make checks payable to STARWATCHER'S SPECIAL OFFER. If payment by VISA or MasterCard, please fill in below.

Account # ____ - ______ - ______ - ______ Expr. Date __________

Signature ______________________________________

Copy or carefully remove this coupon for mailing to:

STARWATCHER'S SPECIAL OFFER
5102 Azusa Canyon Rd.
Irwindale, CA 91706

There is much more to the carousel of celestial wonders than shown in ASTROWATCH, where the twelve constellations of the ancient zodiac are featured. In the companion book STARWATCH, in addition to the twelve starfields listed in this book which you hold in your hands, twelve more favorite constellations and their pictograms are shown, and where, when and how to find them:

Orion, Auriga, Ursa Minor, Canis Major, Ursa Major, Hercules, Lyra, Cygnus, Pegasus, Andromeda, Cassiopeia and Perseus.

Zodiac Sunsign (CONSTELLATION)	Sun in Starfield (CULMINATION AT MIDDAY)	Culmination Dates FOR STARFRAMES AT MIDNIGHT	Astrology Dates FROM THE LOS ANGELES TIMES
Pisces	Mar. 11–Apr. 20	Oct. 1–Nov. 1	Feb. 20–Mar. 20
Aries	Apr. 20–May 17	Oct. 15–Nov. 15	Mar. 21–Apr. 19
Taurus	May 17–Jun. 21	Nov. 15–Dec. 15	Apr. 20–May 20
Gemini	Jun. 21–Jul. 17	Dec. 15–Jan. 15	May 21–Jun. 21
Cancer	Jul. 17–Aug. 10	Jan. 15–Feb. 15	Jun. 22–Jul. 21
Leo	Aug. 10–Sep. 18	Feb. 15–Mar. 15	Jul. 22–Aug. 21
Virgo	Sep. 18–Nov. 1	Apr. 15–May 15*	Aug. 22–Sep. 22
Libra	Nov. 1–Nov. 22	May 1–Jun. 1*	Sep. 23–Oct. 22
Scorpius	Nov. 22–Nov. 30†	Jun. 1–Jul. 1*	Oct. 23–Nov. 21
Sagittarius	Dec. 17†–Jan. 19	Jul. 1–Aug. 1*	Nov. 22–Dec. 21
Capricorn	Jan. 19–Feb. 16	Aug. 1–Sep. 1*	Dec. 22–Jan. 20
Aquarius	Feb. 16–Mar. 11	Aug. 15–Sep. 15*	Jan. 21–Feb. 19
	*DATES AND TIMES ADJUSTED FOR DAYLIGHT SAVING TIME. †Nov. 30–Dec. 17: Sun is in Ophiuchus.		

Here is a wallet-size card you can photocopy or cut out and carry with you in your pocket. This way you can establish the true "astrological sign" of any of your friends or neighbors.

This chart is from *Astrowatch* by Ben Mayer, published by Perigee Books (New York, 1988).

Name ______________________________

Address ____________________________

City ____________ State _____ Zip _____